DAREDEVILS OF SASSOUN

Armenian General Benevolent Union
Golden Jubilee Publication

DAREDEVILS
OF
SASSOUN

Sasowntsí

The Armenian National Epic

by

LEON SURMELIAN

Illustrated by

PAUL SAGSOORIAN

ALAN SWALLOW
Denver

© 1964 by Leon Surmelian

Library of Congress Catalog Card Number: 64-66183

Other books by Leon Surmelian

I Ask You, Ladies and Gentlemen

98.6°

CONTENTS

INTRODUCTION

THIS RECITAL of the legendary deeds of four generations of strong-men in a warrior community in the Armenian highlands is in the tradition of heroic folktales that dramatize the story of a whole nation and voice its deepest sentiments and aspirations, but un-like such well-known epics as *Gilgamesh*, the *Iliad* and the *Odys-sey*, *Shah-nameh*, *Beowulf*, *Chanson de Roland*, *Poema del Cid* and others one might mention, it has survived solely by word of mouth, transmitted from one generation to another by village bards.

The written literature of Armenia goes back to the fifth cen-tury of our era, its "Golden Age," when the Bible was translated into the vernacular from the original Greek and Syriac texts, Plato and Aristotle were studied in Armenian schools, and many original works of great interest to the modern specialist were produced by native historians, philosophers and poets. The oral literature is older than the written, and folk poetry had flourished in Armenia for the past two thousand years, not to go farther back. Movses Khorenatsi (Moses of Khoren) tells us in his classic History of Armenia (fifth century) that Armenians still loved the old pagan "songs" the minstrels sang on festive occasions, and he quotes from them. Only these fragments — and they are charming — have survived. There must have been hundreds of these songs.

Songs celebrating memorable events have retained their hold on the popular imagination, and we might say that Armenians are preeminently a nation made by the book and the folk song, the word, written and spoken or sung, forging the consciousness of the race. But the spoken word is more perishable than the written, and little has survived. Yet, even this little is impressive.

The story of Sassoun — the greatest achievement of the oral literature — was "discovered" in 1873 by a bishop of the Armenian Apostolic Church, Garegin Servantstian, who had exceptionally close contacts with the peasantry in the more remote inaccessible parts of western Armenia, where life had not changed much for a thousand years or so. He says: "For three years I tried to find somebody who knew the entire story, but nobody seemed to know all of it until I met Gurbo from a village on the plain of Moush. I learned that his master had two pupils who also knew the tale by heart, singing the verses in it, although Gurbo himself had not recited it for so long that he had forgotten a good deal of it. Nevertheless I kept him with me for three days, I begged him, cajoled him, honored him, rewarded him, and when he felt better and was in the proper mood he recited the tale for me in his own village dialect, and I wrote it all down in his own words."

The tale told by Gurbo was published in Constantinople, in 1874, under the title, *David of Sassoun or Meherr's Door*. To quote the bishop again: "The life of David and his exploits belong to the Middle Ages. . . . The entire story is a record of courage, of domestic virtue, of piety and of simple open-hearted relations with his beloved woman as well as with his enemies. Despite its irregularities and anachronisms it has some fine stylistic qualities and narrative devices in it. . . . The publication of this tale would be of interest to the understanding reader, but I suppose there will also be those who will express their contempt for it and abuse both the story and my own person. These readers will not understand it. But it does not matter. I shall consider myself encouraged if I find twenty sympathetic readers."

In those days Armenians attached little importance to their oral literature. The country was divided between the Turkish and Russian empires, and there were two nations in each sector. The more prosperous and cultivated Armenians in the western sector living in Constantinople and the larger provincial towns preferred the works of French authors. By 1874 a literary renaissance was in the making and Armenians were rediscovering their past, but the young poets liked to write French verse in Armenian; many still do. Why bother with *David of Sassoun or Meherr's Door* when they could read Balzac and Victor Hugo? And similarly, in Tiflis, where sat the Russian viceroy of the Caucasus, and in other Russian cities where Armenians had reached a relatively high cultural level they derived their intellectual nourishment from Pushkin and Lermontov, from Gogol, Turgenev, Tolstoy, Dostoevski, or from West European epics in Russian translation. How could a tale in a crude village dialect be literature?

But the good bishop started a movement that slowly bore fruit. Gurbo's tale was translated into Russian in 1881. Since then the fame of the Sassoun warriors has slowly spread in Russia, and today it is familiar reading matter in all fifteen republics of the Soviet Union, and Russians, Ukrainians, Byelorussians, Georgians, Azerbaijan Turks, Uzbeks, Kazakhs and others can read it in their own language. In the Armenian SSR everyone knows David of Sassoun; he is the national hero. Recent translations have been in Chinese and French.

Garegin Servantstian was born in Van, in 1840, and so he knew the locale of the story well, growing up in the vicinity of Meherr's Door with its wedge-shaped cuneiform inscriptions. Van is situated on the eastern shore of Lake Van, and is famous for its citadel-rock and gardens and orchards and channels of running water in the streets. He has left some vivid descriptions of his native city and its surroundings. This beautiful mountain lake, eighty miles long and forty miles wide, and more than a mile above sea level, was holy to the bishop, and holy were the flora and fauna of this historic region. Van is the oldest city in Armenia, and was the capital of Urartu, which was engaged in fierce wars with the Assyrian empire until with the invasion of the Indo-European Armenians from the west Urartu became known as Armenia, about 600 B.C. So Van is older than Armenia itself. It is one of the oldest cities in the world still inhabited, and perhaps the oldest, next to Damascus, which claims to be the oldest.

He was ordained a bishop in my home town, Trebizond (founded by Greek colonists and already an old outpost of Hellenism at the time of Xenophon and his Ten Thousand), and he served as the Armenian prelate of Trebizond. My maternal grandfather, Ohannes (John) Diradourian, as a leading patriotic merchant was closely associated with him in the management of the prelacy affairs. The bishop, by virtue of his office, was both the religious and civil head of our community in Trebizond. He was also a dedicated teacher, and I learned to read and write in the school which became a progressive institution under his supervision and a foyer of national sentiments. I began to study French in the third grade, and like other Armenian schoolboys I wanted to go to Sassoun and fight for its freedom. Sassoun was still in rebellion. My favorite teachers had been the bishop's students.

I sang in the choir of the church where the bishop had preached many of his memorable sermons. One day, when I was about three years old, my mother took me to this church and had the key of its door placed in my mouth to "open" it. I learned to speak rather late, and I stuttered. "God's key opened your mouth," my mother used to tell me, though at times she wished it had not. I was a noisy child, and imitated the sermons of another ecclesiastic, holding a broomstick as my episcopal crozier.

From Trebizond Garegin Servantstian was transferred to a more important post and became the pastor of the Holy Trinity church in Constantinople, and meanwhile taught in the Armenian Central Lycée. I was attending this lycée when I came to America, and I went to this church regularly every Sunday and sang in the choir. I wrote my first Armenian poems in the schoolrooms where he had taught, and in the Pangalti cemetery where he was buried in 1892, in a churchyard. This cemetery was near the Essayan orphanage where I was given food and shelter while studying at Central Lycée – and much of the food we ate came from America. I lived on bread made from American flour, on cocoa and condensed milk generously given to us by our American friends of the Near East Relief, and I wore the discarded patched-up uniform of an American soldier. There were ten thousand Armenian war orphans in the city, and I was one of them. The cemetery was our playground, and I used to wander, alone, among the tombstones, murmuring verses, and I often used a marble tombstone as a desk to write on.

Vahan Tekeyan, then the dean of living Armenian poets, published my little poems in the newspaper he edited, not knowing their author was a mere schoolboy of sixteen. Meanwhile he was appointed to be the new dean of the Lycée I attended, which was the leading educational institution of western Armenians in Turkey, and, when we met, that great man tried to persuade me to be a poet in earnest. (I thought I was playing a hoax, my real purpose was to find influential friends who could help me to come to America to study agriculture, as I have told in *I Ask You, Ladies and Gentlemen.*) I argued with Vahan Tekeyan about the importance of agriculture, I said we had to start again with the soil, with the holy and eternal soil, we had to go back to the village, I did not care to be a poet, when he urged me to leave agriculture to others and to concentrate on writing poetry.

I mention it here because my enthusiasm for the village — I was a city boy — sprang in part from *David of Sassoun* and other writings of Bishop Garegin Servantstian I had read and pondered on. The bishop had been the secretary of Khrimian Hairik, and was closely associated with him in Van. Khrimian endeared himself to his people and was affectionately called Hairik, "Little Father." Both were men of the people, men of the soil, and started a back-to-the-land movement among Armenians. Back to the native land, the holy and eternal soil of Armenia. Khrimian rose to the highest post in the church, that of Catholicos and Supreme Patriarch of All Armenians, whose residence is at Holy Etchmiadzin, the Mother-Monastery, at the foot of Mt. Ararat, near Erevan. I was working out a philosophy of agriculture based, emotionally, on the writings of Khrimian Hairik. I thought the future of Armenia depended on me. Such is age sixteen. . . .

II

OTHER VARIANTS of this folk epic have been published since 1874, and there are some fifty of them altogether. If Garegin Servants- tian saved the Armenian epic from oblivion, sixty years later Dr. Manouk Abeghian of the Armenian Academy of Sciences rendered an almost equally valuable service with his co-workers by collecting nearly all these variants in three scholarly volumes published by the State Publishing House in Erevan in 1936, 1944, and 1951, under the general title *Daredevils of Sassoun (Sassna Dzurer)*. We have in these three volumes (the third vol- ume is Part II of Volume II), edited by Dr. Abeghian, with the collaboration of Professor Karapet Melik-Ohanjanian, over 2,500 pages of text. In 1939 a collated text weaving most of the important episodes together was published for popular reading under the title *David of Sassoun*. A second edition of this book appeared in 1961, with a long introduction by the late Joseph Orbeli of the Armenian Academy of Sciences, who acted as general editor. The aim of the scholars who worked on this collated text was not to produce a serious scientific work. They wanted to popularize this heroic tale, and succeeded in that purpose. So far all translations have been made from it. I went directly to the original village stories for this English version.

The combined text for popular reading was the first attempt of its kind, and somewhat experimenal by its very nature. As village texts are in various dialects, which present many difficulties to the modern reader, the story was reworded and a fairly uniform style comprehensible to eastern Armenians was adopted. Most of the variants are in western Armenian dialects, and Sassoun itself is in western Armenia, in the rugged mountain country southwest of Lake Van — in what is actually eastern Turkey today. I cannot help feeling that the scholars who produced *David of Sassoun* as a unified narrative paid more attention to linguistic problems, grammatical forms, dialect words, spelling, pronunciation, rhythm, etc. — their specialties — than to structure and plot. These are valuable contributions to a better understanding of the story, but I believe the time has come for the "historical" school to be superseded by the artistic. Now that the linguistic and critical ground has been cleared up — though some problems remain — the poets ought to take over. The poet's unifying vision can organize this vast material into a more luminous whole. The choice and arrangement of the episodes, to use an Aristotelian term, is the "soul" of this tragedy. And plot and language are so closely connected that the same sensibility, the same vision, is at work in both.

The literary merits of the Sassoun saga surpass its value as a historical or linguistic document. Today the poetics of the work should be explored — how it is made, how it is put together, the arrangement of the episodes, characterization, dialogue, style, recognition and reversal scenes, the proportion of scene and summary, its dramatic immediacy, the point of view or voice structure, and so on. Some highly significant episodes are missing in *David of Sassoun*. The section on Little Meherr, for instance, the fourth cycle, or branch, is fragmentary and inadequate. It does not do justice to the original texts, and could be twice as long. Some subtle thematic overtones are overlooked. The religious motif is played down. Many of the transitions are awkward. There are certain departures from the original texts which are of questionable value to me. Significant story elements are neglected, and there is a general lowering of the poetic tone and content of the story compared to the original texts collected in the three volumes I mentioned. I hope these defects will be corrected when the work is revised, as it should be, and the problem of a popular edition of the Sassoun saga is approached from a new, artistic point of view. It is now a poet's job.

I said so in Erevan when I returned to Armenia in the summer of 1964 with this English version, while discussing the epic with poets and professors, in the official *Literary Gazette (Gragan Tert)*, on radio and television. Armenia's capital is a city of intense literary activity and the *Literary Gazette* is sold in the streets like a popular weekly newspaper. I found that my own views on *Sassoun* are shared by others. As one writer and professor said with a smile, "We may translate your English version into Armenian." I have approached the subject as an Armenian poet, determined nevertheless not to make this a "literary treatment" of the epic. It is the first attempt to produce not only the English, but also a poetic, version of *Sassoun* in its entirety.

Armenians cherish their national epic. It is the most highly treasured possession in the archives of the Abeghian Institute of Literature of the Armenian Academy of Sciences. When you talk with the Director of the Institute, Doctor-Professor Gourgen Hovnan, you can see that this is a sort of national holy of holies that must be preserved in all its purity and cannot be tampered with. I am grateful to him and to other specialists on his staff for critical readings of my manuscript and for many valuable suggestions.

Today we do not read the Homeric poems for their historical interest, great as it is. We read them because we enjoy them, they are good stories. Similarly, in the saga of Sassoun we are dealing with a narrative poem Armenians have enjoyed for centuries.

Homer no doubt was widely read in ancient Armenia. Greek was the language of the Armenian aristocracy and court. Armenia was a Hellenistic state before the introduction of Christianity that linked her definitely with the West, and as Plutarch tells us in his life of Marcus Crassus the King of Armenia, Ardavasd(es), was so expert in Greek language and literature that he wrote tragedies and histories and orations in Greek, some of which were still extant in Plutarch's time. Plutarch vividly describes the presentation of the *Bacchae* by Euripides in Armenia during the wedding festivities celebrating the marriage of Ardavasd's sister to a son of the Parthian king, when Rome was at war with Parthia. The head of the Roman triumvir was brought to the Armenian capital and thrown into the banquet room, and the actor Jason seized it, says Plutarch, and playing the part of a bacchante in her frenzy sang in a rapturous voice:

> We have hunted down a mighty chase today
> And from the mountain bring the noble prey . . .[1]

Evidently during the wassails of the Armenian aristocracy there were dramatic performances and recitations in Greek, and troupes of Greek actors were engaged to play in the royal theatre of Armenia, or to entertain guests at a drinking party. We may assume that Homer too was recited on these occasions.

If so, has Homer influenced the development of the Armenian epic? It is an intriguing question. We find forty riotous suitors in the hall of the lady Khandout, as in the House of Odysseus, and in a few variants David slaughters all forty of them before he marries the princess. We find, as in the Homeric poems, that a guest is fed first and then questioned about his family and city and the purpose of his visit; that "seven cities" are given as reward; hands are washed ceremoniously before meals; solemn oaths are sworn, which cannot be broken; champions fight in single combat; sparks fly from the hooves of horses that seem to fly between heaven and earth, so swift are they; the mouths of caves are closed with big rocks or millstones, and monsters or demons may live in them; articles of clothing are kept carefully in chests; armor and weapons are the same; the warrior is expected to be a great drinker of wine, given to loving and feasting — the list can be extended.

We should remember in this connection that Homer himself was born in Asia Minor, the Trojan war was fought in Asia Minor, and it is not at all unlikely that Homer and his predecessors among the Greeks drew upon a common source of story material known from one end of Asia Minor to the other, from the towers of Ilium to the rocky citadel of Van. And the same may be said about any possible influence the Iranian Book of Kings, *Shahnameh*, may have had on the Sassoun saga, though here the relationship seems closer. We find in both epics champion wrestlers of superhuman strength and of such massive weight that their feet sink into the earth; uprooted trees used as weapons in battle; a deadly combat between father and son; falling into wells, etc. But, the hero of *Gilgamesh* also was a champion wrestler. Once you start tracing influences, you are likely to go back to Babylonia and into the farthest misty reaches of Near Eastern mythology. And the modern reader will note, too, a certain similarity between the Armenian David and the David of the Bible, and the combat with Misra Melik reminds us of David's battle with Goliath.

Such speculations would carry us far and lie outside the scope of this brief informal introduction. There can be no question about the distinctly national character of the Armenian epic. It is a unique work of folk art, created by the native vision, shaped by historic events. Only a country like Armenia, caught between

East and West and wholly belonging to neither, a battleground of world empires, of Christendom versus Islam, and a mediator between two seemingly irreconcilable civilizations and ways of life, yet uniting more than separating — only Armenia, I say, could produce *Sassoun*. And in reading this story we have no difficulty in going from the personal to the national to the universal.

III

THIS EPIC is known among Armenians under various titles: *Sassoun's Strongmen* (*Sassna Pahlevanner*); *David of Sassoun* (*Sassountsi Davit*); *David and Meherr* (*Davit yev Meherr*); *House of the Great* (*Chochants Doun*); or the title describes a cycle: *Sanasar and Balthasar* (*Sanasar yev Baltasar*). But among the reciters themselves and in the original published texts the most common title is *Daredevils of Sassoun*. Sassoun may be spelled Sassoum. It may be *Sassna* or *Sassma Dzurer*.

In the country districts where the "other half" of the nation lived, in the villages of Van and Moush, and in Sassoun itself, people cherished the memory of these fools, and fortune did favor them. People loved these eccentrics who broke the rules and did the impossible. The word *dzour*, "twisted," "mad," "cracked," "wacky," has connotations of courage and heroism, of reckless adventures by dashing fellows, and is used as an affectionate epithet in all variants of the story. The Armenian is *dzour* to begin with, he is mad, and he has survived by breaking the rules of history. He is a wild rebel by nature, a wild rebel with a dream. In Armenia we have the Don Quixote of nations. Armenians everywhere have taken to heart these indomitable and unpredictable screwballs of Sassoun who symbolize the magnificent crazy streak in the nation. These mountain giants deviate from the normal, the straight path is not for them, they will not play it safe, they will not do the conventional thing — and this quality has endeared them to other Armenians, who often had to bow before the inevitable, even if their submission to brute force was temporary and the national spirit was never wholly broken. The history of Armenia has been a series of insurrections and resurrections.

These Armenian supermen with their "twisted" minds may be called the beatniks of the Middle Ages. They are unconventional daredevils, the possessed of Christian Armenia refusing to be drowned in successive tides of pagans, and the *dzour* may be a titanic warrior as well as a fool in the more common meaning of the word.

The men who wrote this story down — in some variants we do not even have the name of the reciter and writer — had the good sense not to convert it into standard literary Armenian. The particular village idiom is an internal evidence of the authenticity of the tale, although we may assume the writers organized and edited the material before it was published in some journal or in book form, and these original texts are not stenographic reports, or tape recordings. They would lose much of their charm in the current literary idiom. These village dialects are full of Persian, Arabic and Turkish words, and some of the native words in this peasant language are close to English — *pop*, *mom* (spelled with "a"), *sol* (shoe), *nané* (old woman, translated here as nanny). I changed pop and mom to father and mother, lest the reader think the English used in this translation is too colloquial for an Armenian epic. In this medieval tale the language itself is not medieval, but modern spoken Armenian, in various country dialects. There are many similarities between Armenian and English because both are Indo-European languages.

These village dialects have all but disappeared today. Some of them are preserved in the variants of this saga written down after 1930; another ten or fifteen years would have been too late. It is an uncommon language today, and becomes distinctive and poetic by that very fact. If we were to remove these words and expressions no longer in use among Armenians in and out of Armenia for greater clarity, the story of Sassoun would go flat. On the other hand in an English translation like this one the language is still uncommon enough, in spots, such as in dialogue, to make it distinctive for the English-speaking reader, and thus some of the poetic flavor of the original texts is restored in translation.

One cannot help but admire the simplicity, the sober dignity, the economy of expression, the color of rustic metaphors and analogies, the vivid imagery, and the quiet impersonal tone of these village reciters. You have to be on the alert not to miss a significant point or an important event told in a line or two. In variant after variant it is a tight, compact style, pictorial and concrete, with few abstract words, and sometimes none. It is a rhythmic energetic tongue admirably suited to this kind of oral tale told by villagers, and all it lacks perhaps is melody. The rough consonants pile up and it is much harsher in its sound patterns than literary Armenian. These peasants speak with rocks in their mouths.

Though this language abounds in poetic pictures it lacks the rich poetry of the Homeric epics. The physical sensory details are often missing. But we should remember that the language of an oral tale is necessarily different from that of a written story. The reciter must get on with his action to hold the interest of his audience, plot is the main thing, and the reciter suits the word to the action. There is no emotional heightening of the event through language, there is no sentimentality, there are no purple passages. It's a beautifully controlled language and everything is understated, although hyperbole is a necessary and characteristic device of this epic style. The audience, you may be sure, hugely enjoys the exaggerations. The story of Sassoun is built on a larger scale than life, and both heroes and their actions are magnified. The language of the peasants is meager and cut down to the bone, the adjectives and adverbs are few, but there is no limit to the striking power of David's sword, made invincible by God, and when the thirsty Arabs reach the river on the border of Armenia it dries up, and they are as number-less as the stars in heaven. These exaggerations do not falsify the story. It is a legitimate emphasis. And does make for economy in description.

The reciter has to use a language comprehensible and pleasing to his audience, and he cannot improvise and invent new incidents to fill the gaps in his memory or in the action, or to give a new interpretation of what took place. The audience knows the story and will not tolerate a change. It is a "sin" to add anything, to make up, to mix it with other tales, and the virtuosos among these storytellers can repeat it word by word from beginning to end. They learn it by heart and it is like reciting the Lord's Prayer. It is a sacred tale to them and its recitation a public event in the community. You cannot get up and leave before it is over. Not a few are professional reciters and may act as local historians. Some have a strain of mysticism in their makeup, and like the rhapsodists of the Homeric poems recite and sing this epic in a state of ecstasy.

Yet no two variants are exactly alike. The story has migrated from one village to another, from one part of Armenia to another, and has undergone various changes during these migrations. Some variants contain all four "branches" of the tale, and others are limited to the story of Sanasar and Balthasar, or David and Misra Melik. The complete stories are relatively few, and you have to stitch them together to get the full picture. And that is what I have done in *Daredevils of Sassoun*, taking care not to leave out a single important detail or significant episode, and adding nothing.

Gurbo of Moush had his equals or superiors in Nakho, Sasho, Rasho, Azo; rustic names that sound a bit Kurdish today. These unlettered peasants, totally illiterate or barely able to sign their names, are esteemed in their mountain hamlets — or were, I should say, for Armenians no longer live in Sassoun, or Van, or Akhlat, or Moush. The native Christian population of the western sector was finally wiped out by the Turks during the first world war. But true to their historic tradition the people of Sassoun, and of Van, fought back, and the survivors managed to reach Caucasian Armenia, under Russian rule, and helped establish in 1918 an independent Armenian republic, now the Armenian SSR — just as in 901, according to an ancient chronicle, "Fifty princes of Sassoun, hard-pressed by the Turks, moved to Cilicia and with the help of God conquered that country little by little."

These fifty princes of Sassoun, with other knights, notably of the Roubenian dynasty, founded a new Armenian kingdom on the shores of the Mediterranean when Great Armenia itself was overrun by the "Nation of the Archers." Medieval Armenia spread from the snowy peaks of the Caucasus to Tarsus, the birthplace of St. Paul, and the Gulf of Alexandretta. It was engaged in continuous wars with Turks and Arabs and fought with the Crusaders for the liberation of the Holy Places. The new kingdom lasted until 1375, when it was overcome by the Mamelukes of Egypt, and the last King of Armenia, Leon V de Lusignan, was taken to Cairo by the victors and kept a captive until his ransom was paid by the Kings of Castile and Aragon. The Armenian King was welcomed to England by King Richard II as an envoy of France and spoke to the assembled lords in Westminster Palace, pleading for peace between the two great powers of the West, so that with united efforts the Christians of the West could liberate the Christians of the East. Leon V died in exile in Paris.

The cross went down before the crescent, but the light of Sassoun kept burning through the darkness that fell over Christian Armenia. In 1459-60 the "Republics" of Sassoun and Ghitharane, apparently the Latinized name of the adjoining province of Khouth, sent ambassadors to Western Europe to renew the Armenian-Latin alliance. These gentlemen, Hetoum and Rouben, traveled to Rome by way of Hungary and Germany. *"Haitone et Rubino, ambascadore dell republiche de Ghitharane et Sassoni"* as they are described in a contemporary chronicle,[2] were received by Charles VII and his son Louis XI of France.

Pope Pius II was trying to organize a new crusade and the aid of Armenians also was sought for the recovery of Constantinople, which the Turks took in 1453, and the delivery of Jerusalem. This new crusade was to be led by Philip the Good, Duke of Burgundy, then the head of the most prosperous state in Europe; and the Emperor of Trebizond, the King of Georgia, and even an infidel, Uzun Hassan, "Long Hassan," chief of the Turkoman tribe of the White Sheep, whose wife, the lady Theodora, was a Greek princess of Trebizond and a niece of the Emperor David, were to take part in it. It never got under way. The Turks were in Trebizond in 1461, and no effective Christian force could be organized against them. The Turks under Mohammed II became the first military power of the world. But Sassoun was never fully subdued by the Turks, it remained rebellious, and the invincibility of Sassoun is part of the Armenian legend celebrated in ancient visions and prophecies and in this epic.

The later versions of this heroic tale were written down in Caucasian Armenia, narrated by survivors of massacres and guerilla fighting, or the story had previously migrated to the Caucasus. Most of these village reciters were wretchedly poor, hounded and persecuted by government men, or harassed by their immediate neighbors, the warlike Kurds, who as Moslems were favored by the Turkish administration and armed and organized into cavalry regiments to keep the Armenians in line, and to resist a new Russian thrust southward. These folk-poets often left their homes and sought refuge on the other side of the border, or went to Constantinople to work as hamals (porters), carrying huge loads on their sturdy backs, and glad to have a loaf of bread and a raw onion or a few olives for lunch or supper.

Many of those who stayed home earned their daily bread as shepherds and tillers, or as weavers, millers, masons, blacksmiths, and numbers of them traveled around with their buzzing bows to spin wool and cotton. Almost the first question these spinners were asked on arriving at a village was, "Can you tell stories?"

If there was a man in the group who could spin yarns on long winter nights, the group prospered. They were given work, good food, a warm room to sleep in. A master story-teller among these migrant workers could hold his audience spellbound, and songs added to the effect. These songs are chanted in a grave monotonous melody steeped in the sadness of the East. Their repertoire is not limited to the Sassoun story, but this is the great favorite.

It may be that originally this tale was entirely in verse, and verse of course is easier to remember. Measured speech makes for longer life in oral literature. Dr. Manouk Abeghian and his coworkers gave a new linear arrangement to the variants included in the three volumes I mentioned to make them read like free verse, or at least look like verse. Obviously the language in all these variants though completely devoid of bookish words is not the normal daily idiom of Armenian peasants and is poetic to begin with, and the linear appearance strengthens this impression, but most of the original texts are in prose, only the songs being in verse. These songs are lyrical outbursts, loosely metrical, and the rhyming is irregular, a characteristic feature being the repetition of words or lines. Armenian, like French, and unlike English, is not a highly accented language and the accent normally falls on the last syllable, and what we usually have in these songs is iambic verse, pure or mixed, with so many syllables per line. I have used 4 + 4 or 5 + 5, which are common in Armenian and in the original texts of this epic. These passages in verse are generally sung by the reciters. They are meant to be sung. Some of the characters themselves sing during the course of the action. And it is in these songs that the language and form of the epic are preserved with relatively few changes.

IV

THIS HEROIC story has dramatic unity and is an integrated organic whole, with the basic conflict, the struggle against the foreign invader, sustained from beginning to end, and causal connections tying the parts together. I can assure you that all the episodes in *Daredevils of Sassoun* may be found in the original texts and no incident is invented in order to fill a gap in the action, for instance. There was no need for it, the plot is complete in itself, and if there is a gap in one variant the missing fragment can be found in another variant. Nor is any part of the dialogue invented. Again, there was no need for it.

Much of the story is told in dialogue. It is authentic peasant speech, brief, pointed, with no unnecessary repetitions, and the treatment of the story is consistently scenic. We have a succession of moving pictures and not static tableaux. The reciters stick to the immediate scene with direct dialogue and there are virtually no retrospective narrations, so that the method is astonishingly "modern." And the thought and feelings of the characters are given in their own words. We get glimpses into the internal world of the central figures, we know what they are thinking and feeling at critical moments in the action through their silent unspoken speech and songs voicing their innermost sentiments. The reciters seldom make any comments on the action, they refrain from expressing their personal opinions in keeping with the impersonal tone of the narrative, and they let the audience judge the action for itself. Evidently this is their natural instinctive way of telling a story, and it is craftsmanship of a high order. We have an object lesson in the art of narration, the construction of a story on dramatic principles.

The central figures are not aristocrats as in other national epics. We are in a typical peasant community, and even the "princes" of Sassoun, unnamed, are just simple villagers like the other inhabitants of this city-state. Sassoun is both a town and a region taking in considerable territory, bordering on Egypt in the south, or Misr as Egypt is invariably called by its Arabic name, and Misr too is both a city and a state. Geographically it is not Egypt proper but the Syrian and Iraqi region; Cairo is too far away. There is no discernible class structure in Sassoun and David goes through the usual routine of being a shepherd and drover. It is a busy working community where labor is respected and the building trades and other crafts flourish. Sassoun is pure democracy. We have a village republic here presided over by Uncle Toros and Uncle Ohan. The kings are on the other side. The Armenians are, one and all, democrats, equals among equals. They are free proud peasants who will not pay tribute and taxes to alien monarchs — and the tribute-tax theme runs through the entire action and with the religious conflict forms the basic story line in this saga.

These are simple Christians devoted to their monastery high up on the crags, and just as Sassoun symbolizes Armenia as a whole, "Marouta's High Mother of God" symbolizes Sassoun. The sacred name of their monastery is their battle-cry. But these Christian warriors are not ascetics. They appreciate physical beauty and are not immune to the pleasures of the flesh. With all their devotion to the Cross they display an exuberant joy in earthly life. There are monks, but they are not among the central figures and take no direct part in the action.

These Armenian strongmen are not engaged in private wars, for selfish ends. They are all patriots, ready to sacrifice their lives for the welfare of their community and nation. They are engaged in the world-wide conflict of Christianity vs. Islam, carrying the Christian battle-flag all the way to Baghdad and Egypt, and they mercilessly slaughter the heathen hordes that cross the border, but they have their own heroic and gallant code and it is never indiscriminate slaughter of the enemy. David warns the Egyptian army before he attacks, he does not want to be accused of sneaking in on them while the Egyptians are asleep at their camp and fires are burning; he is opposed to killing prisoners of war, and his quarrel is not with the Egyptian people but with the tyrant who rules over them. One of the most revealing episodes in the entire narrative is David's encounter with the old Arab warrior with seven sons in Misra Melik's army. David's son Meherr calls the forty princes of Aleppo his brothers and fights for the King in Baghdad. David and Misra Melik are half-brothers and have the same father, Lion-Meherr, or Great Meherr. This kinship is further emphasized by intermarriage. Sara, the Phaedra in this tale, says repeatedly, "I am a foreign woman." Khandout Khatoun is not an Armenian woman, as we can tell by her name. Her family is pagan, though she herself is conveniently Christian. As in *Chanson de Roland*, the Moslems are called pagans, and in Armenia, under Moslem rule, the reciters had to be prudent and not call the enemy by his name. Sanasar, Balthasar, Lion-Meherr, David, Little Meherr, Uncle Ohan — all marry foreign women, or have romantic interludes with them. These Sassounians do not have narrow provincial minds, they are not bigots, but world citizens in their thinking. It is largely from religious motives that they insist on the purity of their stock. The Christian Armenian will not marry a heathen: that is a basic principle in their conduct. He who does not acknowledge the Cross is an enemy. But otherwise there are no national or racial prejudices, and we even meet with considerable religious toleration. They are not Christian fanatics.

All these women, beginning with Golden-Braids in Copper City, a mythical town, assert woman's right to freely choose her husband and to marry for love rather than for some other consideration. And they are warriors in their own right. These women are not harem slaves, but even more emancipated than modern women in the west. The freedom and dignity they enjoy is part of the Armenian mores in this tale; it is never questioned, and is taken for granted as the natural thing, making women more desirable in men's eyes. And indeed, these women take the first step in every courtship. They do not hesitate to write love letters and propose marriage. They are not modest about their charms. They are highly emotional, and can be vindictive. In general, we have the impression on reading this medieval tale that we are not in a primitive society, and on the contrary there is something surprisingly modern about this village community, where women too read and write, and may be even more learned than the men (Khandout Khatoun, Gohar Khatoun).

V

HOW "TRUE" IS IT? Is this history or poetry? It is poetry, and truer and more universal than history would be. It is not a fairy tale. It "happened." The reciters believe in its factual truth in all essentials, for in those days lived giants and anything could happen by God's order, they say. What we have is a symbolic action dramatizing the Arab-Armenian wars during the Middle Ages, and David and the other heroes have their historic prototypes. Many parallels may be drawn between events in the tale and actual historic incidents. If it were pure history we could not have this artistic form and would have at best a loose chronicle of episodes and not an integrated plot. The characters are composite types, idealized portraits, with distinct individual personalities. The marvelous has crept into it, but it is not a placeless and timeless story, as in a fairy tale. Fantasy is a characteristic part of other epics.

The epic form is inherently loose. A tight dramatic plot with a strictly logical development of the action would leave out too much, and the episodic structure is natural to the epic and necessary for sound artistic reasons. The *Iliad* is a less unified work than the Armenian epic, almost arbitrary in the succession of its episodes and confusing in its action, nor does the *Odyssey* have a rigorously logical plot. We cannot expect unlettered peasants to produce an architecturally perfect work, or to speak with the eloquence of Homer, but this saga of Sassoun strikes me as being, with all its imperfections, grander in design and even more universal in its significance than the Homeric epics. This is a more philosophical tale, remarkable for the richness and variety of its episodes. We miss the splendor of Homeric language, but the Armenian epic has its own formal beauty. And when we compare it with other epic tales, with *Chanson de Roland* or *Beowulf*, or with *The Song of Igor's Campaign*, they seem, with all their poetic charm, minor actions. There is more "story" here.

In 1939 Armenians all over the world celebrated the one thousandth anniversary of the Sassoun saga. Like other folk epics it had a long period of gestation and development and reached its present form probably in the twelfth century, but parts of it are older and go back to Biblical times. In Sanasar and Balthasar we have Sarasar and Adramelech, and Sennacherib King of the Assyrians is identified with the Caliph of Baghdad. In Gurbo's version Balthasar is called Abamelik and in other variants the Caliph of Baghdad is Sennacherib, or close to it.

"And Sennacherib king of the Assyrians departing went away: and he returned and abode in Nineveh.

"And as he was worshipping in the temple of Nesroch his god, Adramelech and Sarasar his sons slew him with the sword. And they fled into the land of the Armenians."

(The Fourth Book of Kings, Chapter 19, Douay Bible.)

In the Authorized or King James version (II Kings 19) it's "into the land of Armenia." This event turns up as the climax of a war with the Caliph of Baghdad, and the twins have become the founders of Sassoun. The ancient Armenians eagerly sought Biblical connections for their family trees.

Sanasar and Balthasar have a miraculous birth. Their mother, Dzovinar, is an earthly counterpart of the Holy Virgin, who is the divine protector of Sassoun. Like the heroes of other epics the twins do not belong to the common lot of mortal men. They are not earthborn but waterborn. Their mother drank from a "milk-fountain." These milk-fountains are always located in or near monasteries, and as a child I myself believed in the miracles ascribed to them. Whenever I went to our monastery in Trebizond, built during the Middle Ages, before the Turkish occupation of the city, I always drank from its milk-fountain to be strong and healthy, and to absorb if possible a bit of divine grace. Water is scarce in many parts of Armenia and irrigation is necessary for growing crops, and so water is truly a source of life. In several variants the fountain gushes out of a rock placed in the sea, and the horse, Jalali, also is water-born. Horse and armor come out of the water, and so does the sword Lightning. Horse, armor and sword are passed from father to son, and they are mentioned lovingly in songs that indicate their new possessor has succeeded his father as leader of the Sassoun warriors. They are cherished, item by item, as though these were catalogues of coronation.

In other variants Meherr finds this mighty horse in the stable of his uncle in Bitlis, or David finds it in the cave of the robber demons. No matter what its origin, the horse is always called "fiery." It too belongs to a supernatural order, and is immortal.

The Armenian word for demon is dev, the same word as in divine or deity. These devs are supernatural beings with human attributes. They look and behave like men. They are giants, titans, living in mountain caves, or in forests or deserts — or any inaccessible place. One dev can defeat a thousand men in battle. The dev can hurl boulders as big as mountains. He is a man-eater. He steals the beautiful daughter of a king and holds her captive, but generally the girl manages to remain a virgin by making impossible demands on him. He has to bring her a golden cock or a golden fox or a golden apple from the garden of immortality, or kill a dragon. The devs are the Cyclopes of Armenian mythology. "If you don't behave yourself the devs will come and get you," my mother used to tell me, and like other children I believed in their existence.

The supernatural link is evident also in the name Meherr (Meher). The pagan Armenians were sun-worshippers like the Iranians and Meherr is the native counterpart of the Persian sun-god Mithras or Mithra. Lion-Meherr is a more human and realistic character than Sanasar, his father; the gods are coming down to earth, as it were. And even more human and realistic is David, the main character. The bulk of the story is about David, and David's "branch" is the most extensive, historically true, and lies at the core of the entire narrative. David of Sassoun reminds us of Robin Hood. But with his son, Meherr Junior, the story moves again toward the supernatural, and it may be that both Meherrs are the same person. The genealogy of these strong men is not too certain; we may have three generations and three branches instead of four. A few reciters are said to have known all "forty branches" of the tale, which is by no means improbable, for much has been lost or forgotten, but forty is also a magic number, like seven. Forty kings, forty suitors, forty days, forty thousand.

The second Meherr is a complex, mysterious, contradictory character — and, I think, the most fascinating one. We can easily understand David and sympathize with him, but Meherr Junior makes us wonder. There is both good and evil in him. He is the strongest of all these strongmen. He is a rebel, a vagabond, the wandering Armenian, driven by the furies, as it were. He is dispossessed, and in conflict with evil forces within himself. In the end Meherr Junior, or Little Meherr, towers as a formidable figure whom the earth cannot hold and who waits for judgment day, dreaming of a bright future, a world of peace and plenty. There is something of Sol Invictus about him, the invincible solar god of the old Mithraic cult so much in favor in Roman legions and the most serious rival of Christianity in the last days of paganism. Meherr is the Armenian Prometheus, and perhaps a prototype of the Greek hero who was chained on some Caucasian peak close to Mt. Ararat. The fight of father and son dramatizes in part the battle of generations, and Meherr is made deathless not only because of David's curse, but also because the popular imagination associates him with the old Armenian dream for freedom.

The entire fourth cycle is fragmentary and episodic, with little continuity, and has a distinctly mythological character. The more realistic details of David's story are missing when we come to his son, Little Meherr. The single combat between Little Meherr and Baron Astghik ("Mister Star") has supernatural overtones, as though this were a struggle between two representatives of this invincible solar god. Baron Astghik always strikes from "above" and Little Meherr strikes from "below" and brings him down to earth when he slays him. But it is particularly in its finale that this epic rises to universal heights.

What we have here is an epic struggle for freedom — and the history of Armenia, as of Sassoun, may be summed up in this one word: freedom.[3] It has been a national goal, the Armenian Dream. These screwballs and daredevils fiercely resist any encroachment upon their freedom, and in Sassoun the arch-villain is the tax collector, who represents the King, and the King demands tribute from his subjects. He is not satisfied with gold and silver, he must also have beautiful virgins and women of various sizes. By refusing to pay taxes the Sassounians assert their independence and their dignity as free men.

Armenian peasants were taxed to death, and not always by alien kings, but the foreign rule was incomparably harsher. Not to pay taxes to the Caliphs of Baghdad and their successors, the Kings of Egypt (Misra Melik is a title rather than a name), is a matter of life and death for these peasants trying to eke out a living from their rocky soil. Their ancestors fought against Zoroastrian Persia, and after Persia herself crumbled before the might of the Arabs and was absorbed into the Islamic empire stretching from Granada to Samarkand and India the Armenians continue the old fight for the preservation of their national identity and independence. They never give in.

These irrepressible strongmen who defeat kings have no desire to be kings themselves. Sanasar, Meherr, David, Meherr Junior spurn the crown of a king. They are content to live as peasants. Porridge is a holiday luxury. And in the figure of the old woman, Barav, growing millet and turnips in the little patch of ground she owns, we have the classic picture of the Armenian village with its frugal grandmothers. Barav is a folk figure. She represents the race. The warriors fight victorious wars, but do not enrich themselves with plunder, and remain poor. They do not covet the lands and possessions of other peoples, and they fight only when attacked, and are never the aggressive party.

The Armenian is traditionally a man on horseback. Armenian contingents in Persian armies were composed exclusively of cavalry and sent to guard the Caspian Gates and the Caucasian passes against the Huns and other barbarians. The feudal order flourished in Armenia long before it was established in the West, and the champions of Sassoun are cavaliers living up to the knightly code. Their gallantry extends even to animals. Meherr throws away his sword before he grapples with the lion that will not let anybody pass, because the lion does not carry a sword. David frees the wild animals in the game preserve because they are prisoners, and prisoners should not be killed, he says.

Here is a genuine folk epic still unknown in the west in which we see the rich pageantry of centuries in a storied setting that seems to reverberate with Biblical thunder and lightning when the sword of Sassoun strikes. It strikes for freedom, freedom for all. It strikes for the brotherhood of man, for peace and prosperity. I believe this heroic tale will become a part of world literature. *Daredevils of Sassoun* is at bottom the story of man upon the earth, and in this day and age, a call to greatness.

NOTES

Notes have been reduced to a minimum, not to confuse the reader with unnecessary references to sources or variants, which at best would be of interest only to the specialist familiar with the village dialects the reciters of this epic have used — and he does not need footnotes, he can check details for himself by consulting our source-book, *Daredevils of Sassoun*, Erevan, abbreviated here as *DS*.

[1] From the Modern Library edition of Plutarch's Lives. The wording of this quotation differs in other translations. Shall we call this brutal scene one of the great moments in world drama?

[2] For details see Ashot Hovhannissian's *Chapters in the History of Armenian Liberation Thought*, vol. II, p. 9 (in Armenian). Armenian SSR Academy of Sciences, Historical Institute. Erevan, 1959.

[3] The Greeks considered the Armenians to be of Phrygian stock, and Phrygian means freeman in Greek. Evidently the Armenian language is nothing but a Phrygian dialect according to some modern specialists — and thus the linguistic evidence supports the Greek tradition.

SANASAR & BALTHASAR

Blessed is our merciful Lord.
Have mercy O God on Dzovinar — a thousand mercies!
Have mercy O God on Sanasar — a thousand mercies!
Have mercy O God on Balthasar — a thousand mercies!
Have mercy O God on Golden-Braids — a thousand mercies!
Have mercy O God on Uncle Toros — a thousand mercies!
Have mercy O God on Great Meherr — a thousand mercies!
Have mercy O God on Uncle Ohan — a thousand mercies!
Have mercy O God on Armaghan — a thousand mercies!
Have mercy O God on Lisping David — a thousand mercies!
Have mercy O God on Misra Melik — a thousand mercies!
Have mercy O God on Ismil Khatoun — a thousand mercies!
Have mercy O God on Khandout Khatoun — a thousand mercies!
Have mercy O God on Gohar Khatoun — a thousand mercies!
Have mercy O God on Little Meherr — a thousand mercies!
Have mercy O God on all who listen to my tale.
Have mercy O God on their fathers and mothers.
Blessings to all, the great and small
O merciful Lord.

49723

IT ALL BEGAN with the feud between the Caliph of Baghdad Sennacherib and the King of Armenia. The pious Gagik residing in Blue Castle was an old man of great wealth and many possessions but not blessed with a numerous family and had only one child, a young daughter, Dzovinar by name, whom he adored.

In those days the king who was the strongest made other kings pay him tribute, and the Caliph of Baghdad was the mightiest ruler of all. He gathered his troops and devastated the land of Armenia. King Gagik promised to pay him yearly tribute and taxes and the Caliph returned to Baghdad with many prisoners and much war booty.

After his victory the Caliph sent his deputy and his vizier to collect the tribute and taxes. When they arrived at Blue Castle they saw a wondrous light shining in a window. They stopped and stared at the loveliest maid they ever saw. She glowed as brilliantly as the sun and she seemed to say to the sun: "Stand back, and let me come out and shine in your stead." They swooned on the spot.

Our King sent his men to bring the two Arabs to the castle. They said nothing about tribute and taxes, made no mention of his daughter, and quietly went back to Baghdad.

The Caliph said: "Did you bring the tribute and taxes I imposed on the King of Armenia?"

They said: "O mighty Caliph, may Allah preserve your home, you have all the gold and silver and all the precious stones you want, you have all the land you need, you have more riches and power than any other man on earth and the kings of the world are but your vassals. Why bother with more tribute and taxes when the Christian King of Armenia has a young daughter lovelier than the fourteen-day moon rising from behind seven hills? When you see his daughter you will forget everything, you will not eat and drink, you will do nothing but just look at her day and night. She can give you more joy and happiness than any amount of gold and silver you may receive from her father."

The Caliph stroked his beard and pondered these words of

his deputy and vizier. He sent ambassadors to Blue Castle who said to our King: "We are instructed by our great padishah[1] to inform you that he will deign to marry your daughter."

The King said: "I am Armenian, he is Arab. I am Christian, he is heathen. Our girls do not marry heathens."

The Caliph was furious with this bold answer of his Christian vassal. In his next message he said to our King: "I am coming to put your whole nation to the sword. By Allah I will turn Armenia upside down, I will level the whole country to the ground, I will turn your city into gravel and dust, I will smash your throne and your crown, and when I am through, no trace of Armenia will be left."

The King said: "I will fight. You shall not have my daughter."

The Caliph of Baghdad gathered all his forces, and the rocks of Armenia resounded again with the tramp of Arab armies. They came in countless numbers and spread over the land like the stars in heaven. Many pitched battles were fought and many men were killed on both sides. The Christians fell back before the Arab infantry and horse. The radiant Dzovinar watched the battle from a tower of the castle and sighed: "It's useless, they are too strong for us. It is better that I go of my own will and stop this bloodshed."

She went down to the divan of her aged father and said: "Father, you sit here brooding on this war with the pagan King of Baghdad. I can see it's going against us. If you do not give me to him, I am afraid you will have to give up your kingdom."

The King said: "Yes, my dear child, we are fighting for you, with our backs to the wall. But how can I give you to an Arab when I am Armenian and Christian?"

The young princess said: "If I do not marry this pagan king I will be the cause of so many deaths and so much misery, so many orphans and widows would curse me, that it is better I go perish than see our fair Armenia destroyed."

The King called his councillors and members of his family to a meeting in the divan. They gathered in the great hall, and he said to them: "Shall we give up my darling, or continue the war? What is your opinion in this matter?"

One of his councillors said: "May the King live long, we cannot continue the war much longer, the Arabs have all but destroyed our army. The situation looks hopeless. We have to sue for peace."

"Never," said another councillor. "We shall never surrender. We will fight to the last man. If it were simply a matter of nationality I wouldn't mind, but we recognize the Cross and they are nothing but idolators. It is unthinkable that our young princess, the treasure of our King, should become the wife of a godless, lawless tyrant who, I hear, already has thirty-nine wives in Baghdad, and little Dzovinar will be the fortieth."

Said the queen's brother, Toros, a brave young commander, and a prudent one, a boy of seventeen or eighteen: "May the King live long, let us pretend Dzovinar never existed, we shall try to forget her, much as we love her. We have to sacrifice her to save the nation."

They argued. In the end, the King's bishop gave his consent. The King was too old and feeble to continue the war and sent a message to the Caliph: "Come and take her."

The Caliph was overjoyed. He arrived at Blue Castle with a party of his courtiers and warriors and camped in the flowery meadow near the summer residence of the King. The lady Dzovinar said to her father: "Tell the Caliph I will marry him on one condition only: that I will not be forced to change my religion. I want to live in separate quarters, with a chapel, where I may pray every day, as is our law. Father Melchizedek will go to Baghdad with me as my confessor and spiritual adviser. And after our wedding, the Caliph must not visit me for forty days."

The Caliph readily accepted her conditions. He said to the King: "I give you my solemn word that I will not force your daughter to change her religion. She may continue to worship the Cross. I recognize that there are certain differences between

Arabs and Armenians. Let each side remain true to its own faith. I will not only permit your daughter to live in separate quarters, but I will build a palace for her, opposite mine, with a Christian chapel, as she desires, where she may pray every day, as is your custom. All I want is to marry your daughter and to be known henceforth as the son-in-law of the King of Armenia."

The wedding of the lady Dzovinar to the Caliph of Baghdad was celebrated in Blue Castle for seven days and nights. On Ascension Day, during the wedding festivities, the King let his daughter go to the monastery of Hili with her bridesmaids and an elderly woman who acted as governess. The monastery was crowded with pilgrims, and there was much singing and dancing, drumming and piping. The spring air was filled with the odors of wild flowers. The lady Dzovinar and her friends hiked in the hills and strolled on the seaside, wearing chaplets of wild flowers. They prayed in the monastery and went down to the Milk-Fountain with baskets of food, where they ate on the grass. It was a fountain of immortality, revered by all pilgrims. She became thirsty and drank from it, filling her silver cup; then she drank half a cup more, and before going home knelt before a cross-stone and prayed, with tears in her eyes.

She conceived that day by God's order, and when they put her on a horse and sent her to Baghdad with her husband, who some said was ninety years old, she was already pregnant, though she was only ten or eleven and had not reached yet the age of puberty. Her governess and Father Melchizedek, an old varda-pet² who was her mother's brother, went to Baghdad with her.

The Caliph gave a second and more magnificent wedding for his Armenian bride. The festivities in Baghdad lasted for another seven days and nights. He was a very happy man. He built a separate palace for the lady Dzovinar, with a chapel, as he promised, and he did not visit her for forty days. She could not leave her palace without his permission. She was locked behind seven doors and spent her days in mourning.

She knew after some time she was pregnant, but said nothing, and when the Caliph came to spend a night with her, he drew back in horror when he saw her swollen belly. "It's not from me," he said, and angrily strode out of the bedroom.

He called the vizier to his divan, and asked him what he should do. He suspected the vardapet. This was a plot to pollute his dynasty, with Christian blood. The vizier said: "May the King live long, cut off their heads." The Caliph commanded his executioners to cut off her head. They went to Dzovinar's quarters and said to her: "We have orders from the King to cut off your head."

She said: "I left my father's home a virgin, and a virgin I am to this day. If I am pregnant, it is by God's order. I drank from a fountain of immortality on Ascension Day, and I suppose that's how it happened. Isn't there any law and justice in Baghdad? Doesn't your King know that to cut off the head of a pregnant woman is killing two people, at least one of whom is innocent? Go tell the Caliph what I said. Tell him to wait until my child is born. Let's see, is it a boy, or a girl? I am innocent, I say. I have done nothing wrong."

The executioners reported to the Caliph what the lady Dzovinar said, and he consented to wait until the birth of the child. He said: "We will keep a close watch on her."

Nine months, nine days, nine hours, nine minutes after she drank from the Milk-Fountain the lady Dzovinar gave birth to twins, one bigger than the other. They were secretly baptized on the tonir[3] by Father Melchizedek. The bigger boy was named Sanasar and the small one Balthasar.

When the Caliph saw the twins he did not father he flew into a violent rage and sent his executioners to behead their mother. She said to these swordsmen: "Isn't there any law and justice in this land? Who is going to nurse and take care of these babies if you kill me? Can't you wait a few years, until they grow up? You know it's impossible for me to escape from this palace. I am like a prisoner here."

The executioners went back to the Caliph and reported what she said. He sought again the advice of his vizier. The vizier said: "Give her ten years. She cannot escape."

Sanasar and Balthasar grew as much in one day as other boys did in a year. They took lessons from Father Melchidezek, who taught them to read and write in Armenian, and to read the Bible. One day the Caliph called the twins to his divan and was appalled when he saw how husky, strong and intelligent they were. He talked to them, listened to what they said, and was scared to death.

He said: "What am I going to do with these bastards? What did I do to deserve this punishment? I know that when they grow up they will hang from my beard and cause me no end of trouble. I have to do something before it is too late."

The lady Dzovinar complained she was kept like a caged bird in the palace and the twins were allowed to go with their mother and to play with the other children on the palace grounds under the supervision of royal guards. The other boys ganged up against them, and one day, when the vizier's son called them bastards, and their mother a whore, Balthasar slapped him and broke his neck. "Bastards! Bastards!" all the children shouted, and the twins ran to their mother with tears in their eyes. They asked her, "Who is our father?"

She said: "My dears, your father is the Caliph."

They said: "No, if the Caliph is our father then these boys would not call us bastards."

Sanasar was so upset he wanted to throw himself into the river. "I don't want to live as a bastard," he cried. "Tell me, mother, *who* is my father? I didn't come out of a rock or from under a bush, did I? I must have a father like everybody else."

She said: "I did not want to tell you this, but I would have to sooner or later. My dear sons, you do not have a father, but you are not bastards. The truth is you were not born like other children, but by God's order, and I conceived you on Ascension Day when I drank from the sacred Milk-Fountain of an Armenian monastery. Sanasar is bigger because he came from a full cup of water, and Balthasar was conceived when I drank half a cup. That's why both of you are much stronger than other children, and grow much faster than they."

Sanasar said: "All right, mother, you revealed to us our identity, and now we know how we were born, but who is *your* father?"

She said proudly: "My father is the King of Armenia."

The neck of the vizier's son remained crooked; the royal surgeons could not set it right. The twins were not allowed to go out and play with other boys, they were kept separate from them, but they were happy and cheerful by nature and this was no great punishment for them. Their mother was always sad, always worried, dreading the day when the executioners would come back. On the last day of the ten years' grace granted her by the Caliph she had a special mass said in the chapel, and she and her boys took the holy communion, after which she was ready to die.

When the executioners arrived Sanasar and Balthasar were playing in their room and did not see them. The executioners said:

"We have orders from the Caliph to behead all three of you."

She said, weeping: "Don't talk so loud. I don't want my boys to hear you. Let them play a little longer. These are their last moments on earth. They are so happy. Can't you hear them laughing?"

She asked them to sit down. They said: "We are not allowed to sit down. We don't want to shed your blood in the palace. We have to behead you outside."

She sobbed aloud: "Cut off my head first! Don't behead my boys before my eyes. They are innocent, and so am I. Oh, how can the Caliph be so cruel?"

Her boys heard her. They rushed into the room and saw a few men standing there with swords in their hands. Sanasar asked them: "Who are you? What do you want?"

She whispered to the chief executioner: "Don't tell them. I will go out with you now. I am ready."

The chief executioner said: "Let us go."

Sanasar barred their way. "Mother, where are they taking you?"

She said: "I will be back, son."

"Mother, tell me the truth! I heard you."

She said: "The Caliph has sent these horrible men to cut off our heads."

Sanasar turned to the chief executioner. "*You* are going to cut off our heads?"

He said: "I merely carry out the orders of the Caliph."

Sanasar slapped him so hard the man's head flew off and rolled on the floor, and the gory trunk remained standing. The others dropped their swords and fled.

The Caliph sent the palace guard against the twins, but armed with the swords of the executioners they fought them off and not one soldier could enter Dzovinar's mansion. They cut down half of the troops attacking them and the commander of the royal guard said to the Caliph: "May the King live long, we cannot fight against these demons, we have a couple of mighty pahlevans[4] against us. They are strong enough to knock out your kingdom."

The caliph called off the attack. He said: "Leave them alone. Maybe their mother was right, these are waterborn heroes. Who knows, they may outstrip all earthly men when they grow up. She might be innocent. We shall investigate this matter further, and if she is innocent, I will take her back."

Some time later the Caliph said to the lady Dzovinar: "I am going to take Jerusalem away from the infidels."

He gathered his troops and equipped his army with everything needed for a long siege.

She said: "May you live long, my King, do not go against the Christians."

He said: "Why not?"

She said: "I saw a dream last night."

"What did you dream?"

She said: "I saw a multitude of small stars surrounding one large star that shone brightly. All these small stars fell on the large star, and the large star came hurtling down and fell dead at our door."

He said: "Eh, Dzovinar, do you sleep for yourself and dream for others? I am going to destroy the infidels, I will wipe their race off the face of the earth."

And he arose and went to fight. The Caliph Sennacherib marched on Jerusalem with all his forces and after seven years of fighting defeated the Christians. He drove the survivors into the monastery of Jerusalem and thought not one of them would come out alive. One evening a vardapet said to the people in the church: "We have no bread and no water left and we shall starve to death and die of thirst. Only God can save us from these men."

The vardapet arose and celebrated mass. They all raised their voices to God, they sang hymns and cried until dawn. God sent angels with fiery swords who fell on the Caliph's army and so great was the confusion and the slaughter that the Arabs killed one another. The battle reached the Caliph's tent. He tried to escape on his big Damascus camel. He called on his chief idol to come to his aid. "I vow to offer you forty heifers in sacrifice, if you will save me from these infidels."

But how could his idol help him?

"I will give you all the gold and silver I possess!"

Well, what can you expect from the idols of the pagans? They could do nothing for him.

"O my idols, my idols, help me overcome the infidels and I will offer my sons Sanasar and Balthasar in sacrifice!"

A couple of devils got into his camel and whisked him off to Baghdad. From her window the lady Dzovinar saw him dismount. He had turned pitch-black, and stumbled in a confused, disorderly manner into his palace.

She said: "O my King, may God have mercy on you, you have been gone for seven years, where is your army, where is your commander?"

The Caliph said: "Woman, I had the infidels in Jerusalem at my mercy and they were ready to surrender when they prayed to their God and my army was destroyed with fiery swords that struck us from heaven. I offered forty heifers, all the gold and silver I possess to my god and received no aid from him. Only when I vowed to offer our two sons as sacrifice was I able to save my neck."

She said in her mind: "O my God, he is going to take my two boys to the temple and slaughter them like sheep."

The lady Dzovinar had another dream that night. She woke up her sons and had Sanasar sit on one side of her, his head resting on her knee, and Balthasar on the other side, his head resting on her other knee, and kissed them on their cheeks with tears in her eyes.

The boys asked her: "Mother, why are you crying?"

She said. "I just dreamt of St. Karapet.[5] He came to me and said: 'The Caliph is in great difficulties and will sacrifice Sanasar and Balthasar on the altar of his idols if they don't get out of Baghdad.' My sons, the Caliph knows you are Christians, and he doesn't want a Christian to succeed him on his throne. Tomorrow Saturday he will take you to his temple and slaughter you, so that he may be victorious over the Christians. You must leave Baghdad this very night. Fill a saddlebag with gold coins and another saddlebag with food, and go to my father, the King of Armenia, and ask for his protection."

The boys arose, took up their weapons, and armed with bows and arrows, swords and maces and shields, hurried to the royal stable.

"Bring us a couple of good horses!" they said to the groom.

The horses were brought to them. They kissed their mother on her breast, and said:

"Let the Caliph catch us and sacrifice us to his idols if he can."

And with God's name on their lips they got out of Baghdad before daybreak, and went to Jerusalem. They bowed before the King of Jerusalem seven times, took seven steps backward, clasped their hands on their breasts, and stood at attention before him.

The King asked them: "What can I do for you?"

They said: "O King, we rely on God above, and on you on earth. We came to seek your protection."

"Whose sons are you?"

"We are the sons of the Caliph of Baghdad."

"My boys, I cannot keep you in Jerusalem. We are afraid."

They went to King Moushegh in Moush. They bowed before him seven times, took seven steps backward, clasped their hands on their breasts, and stood at attention before him.

King Moushegh asked them: "Tell me what you need."

They said: "We lack nothing, we only need your protection. We rely on God above, and on you on earth."

"Whose sons are you?"

"We are sons of the Caliph of Baghdad."

"We are afraid of their dead, how can we go against the living? Your father is a most powerful king and if we keep you here he will come and destroy our country."

As they rode away from Moush the twins said: "We shouldn't give that dog's name any more. It is better that we say we have no father, no mother, no country, nothing."

They came to a great river and observed how a little stream came leaping down from the mountains and struck the river with such force that it split it in two, after which their waters mingled and they flowed on together.

Sanasar said: "What a strong stream. Where does it get all its power and spunk?"

Balthasar said: "Very strange. I have been watching it myself. It cuts this great river like a sword."

Sanasar said: "Let's go find its source. This is the right river for a couple of strongmen like us."

They spurred their horses and followed the swirling course of this bold stream, and climbed one mountain after another. Mountains ahead of them and mountains all around them. They rode on day and night, moving through deep gorges and across lofty passes in a towering wilderness. Wild sheep and goats, stag and deer crossed their path. Wild boars crashed through the trees and shrubbery. Hawks circled overhead. Eagles flew over the forests and crags. Finally they found the mouth of the stream they were looking for, gushing out of the rocks. They dismounted and drank its pure refreshing water.

Balthasar said: "The man who drinks this sweet water will grow so strong that nobody can throw him down in a wrestling match. This is a hero's stream, Sanasar!"

Sanasar said: "Beautiful country. We ought to build our house here. This is the place to live."

"Yes, it's a sweet country all right. We ought to come back and build a whole town here."

They unsaddled their horses and lay on the grass beside their little river they named Honeystream. They considered it their own. They still had some food left in their saddlebag. They ate and stretched out on the grass to sleep, with the sound of Honeystream ringing in their ears as it clattered over the rocks and cascaded down the mountain.

The next morning they rode back to the great river in the wooded valley below and continued on their journey until they reached Blue Castle. Their grandfather received them in his divan. They bowed before him seven times, took seven steps backwards, clasped their hands on their breasts, and stood at attention before him.

The hoary King of Blue Castle liked the fiery good looks of these husky blond boys. "Tell me, sons, how is your mother? I have not heard from her for a long time. Tell me what brought you here, tell me everything."

They told him. "Our mother brought us up as Christians," they said. "We are not Arabs or Persians. We came to seek your protection. We rely on God above, and you on earth."

The King got up and kissed them on their heads. "You are welcome in my home. I am proud of you, my lads. This will cause bad blood between the Caliph and me, but you stay."

The twins entered the King's service and worked for a while in the royal stable. The King's groom said:

"Clean the stable and curry the horses."

Balthasar scraped the dirt off the floor and Sanasar swept the stable clean with a broom. Then Sanasar picked up a currycomb — and it crumpled to powder in his hand. The same thing happened with another currycomb. He went around the stable and saw something that looked like a large currycomb. It was a copper trough for watering the horses, filled with barley. He emptied the trough and tried to curry a horse with it. The coat of the horse came off, and it died. By the time the groom came back to the stable all the horses were dead.

"May God wreck your home, you have killed them all!"

He went to the King and told him what happened. He said: "These boys are strong like demons. What shall we do with them?"

The King smiled and said: "I will send them to Green City tomorrow morning to fight the dragon."

In Green City the twins strolled along the streets, and Sanasar said: "What are we going to do in this town?"

Balthasar said: "We will do what God wills."

They met an old woman who befriended them and took them into her home. She said: "I have no sons of my own, you can be my sons, and I will keep you like a mother. God will give us our daily bread."

Balthasar said: "Mamik,[6] I am thirsty, give me some water, please."

The old woman said: "There isn't a drop of water in the house, my child."

He said: "Mamik, what do you mean, there isn't a drop of water in the house?"

The old woman said: "May I die for you, there is no water in Green City. All the fountains are dry. There is a spring on top of that mountain but a dragon sits there and will not let anybody have water.⁷ We can't go near it, we are afraid. Every year we have to take a beautiful virgin to that mountain spring and let the dragon eat her to get some water. Tomorrow it's the turn of another girl to be eaten by the dragon. She has been living in the palace of the King of Green City."

"Mamik, can't you kill the dragon?"

She said: "Son, there is no way of killing it. The King can't do it. A whole army can't do it."

And true enough, the next day the twins saw a young maiden, fair like the moon, and dressed in black from head to foot, being taken to the mountain-spring, followed by women carrying water pitchers and a throng of mourners who cried aloud. The twins joined the procession. When they came out of the city people said to them:

"Take this girl to the dragon and slay it if you can."

The twins had left their horses and weapons with the old woman and said: "We are unarmed."

"Arms have no effect on this dragon."

Balthasar said to Sanasar: "Let's take these two round stones in that big olive press. They have a hole in the center."

The owner complained if the stones were removed from the olive press and carried to the mountain nobody could bring them back, they were so heavy. He himself had moved them to the olive press with a team of buffaloes. The twins said: "We shall bring them back."

They passed their arms through the holes and twirling the stones and playing with them they went to the top of the mountain with the girl and told her: "You stay here. Don't be afraid. We will take care of the dragon."

The girl thought to herself: "I will run away and let the dragon eat them."

They saw her running away. They caught her and tied her to a tree. Sanasar said to his brother: "I had better stay down here, Balthasar, and you go wait for the dragon up there. I am afraid you will not be able to catch my stone when I throw it. We have to be careful not to let these stones roll into the ravine and be lost."

Suddenly the sky clouded, hiding the sun, and the mountains reverberated with an awful roar. The twins turned and saw a monstrous serpent, five buffaloes in length and taller than a buffalo in height gliding furiously toward them. The dragon ground its teeth when it saw that it would have three people for its meal. Flapping its tail and baring its sharp teeth it came toward the girl with its jaws wide open, and breathing fire and hissing with delight. She could not utter a word, she was tongue-tied with fear, and tears streamed down her face. When the dragon came very close and was ready to snatch her away with its huge claws and chew her up Balthasar struck it with his stone. The monster did not fall. Sanasar said, "Hold my stone," and struck next. He smashed the ribs of the dragon. They approached the gigantic serpent and crushed its head under their stones. It writhed in a pool of blood and died. They untied the girl and said: "Now you can go home, you are free."

Water flowed out of the fountains in the city and people rushed to fill their vessels. There was plenty of water now for everybody. The twins took the stones back to the olive press, and returned the girl to the King's palace.

She told the King what happened and related everything she saw. The King said: "Sanasar, Balthasar, tell me what you want as a reward, and you shall have it."

Balthasar said: "We do not want anything."

The King said three times: "I will give you whatever you wish." And Balthasar said three times: "I want nothing."

The King said: "Very well, you do not want a reward for

saving her life, but surely the girl you saved belongs to you. Come, Balthasar, let me marry you two; take her as your wife."

Balthasar said: "I have no time now to marry. We have to go."

They brought the girl in and she was betrothed to Balthasar. The Caliph of Baghdad invaded our country again, but our people, led by Sanasar and Balthasar, drove the invaders back. (This was another holy miracle performed by St. Karapet.) The Caliph fled to Baghdad on his big Damascus camel. The twins caught him during a sacrificial rite in the royal temple in Baghdad, and Sanasar struck off his head with one blow of his sword. The twins smashed up all the idols of the heathen and razed the temple to the ground. They freed their mother, her old governess, and Father Melchizedek. The lady Dzovinar dropped on her knees and thanked God, the creator of heaven and earth, for her deliverance and the victory of the Cross.

Sanasar drew his sword and said: "He who recognizes the Cross let him come pass under my sword."

And people came from all over the city to pass under his sword. They all said: "The God you worship is now our God."

Baghdad submitted to the twins. Sanasar was proclaimed King. But they did not wish to live in Baghdad and returned to Blue Castle with their mother, the old woman and the vardapet. King Gagik and Uncle Toros came out to meet them, and they fell on each other's neck and kissed one another. They laughed, they conversed in joyous voices, and the victory of the Cross was celebrated in Blue Castle for seven days and seven nights.

The old King said to the twins: "My kingdom is yours."

They said: "May the King live long, but we know of a mountain stream where we would like to build our own city."

The King said: "Why should you go live in a rocky wilderness? I am an old man now and I do not have many more years to live. After my death all my lands and possessions are yours."

They said: "May the King live long, thank God, we are free men, and hale and hearty, and we would rather live in our own home. Give us a few poor families, and a few rich ones, to go with us, and at nights we can get together and talk and tell stories and we shall not feel lonely."

The King was moved by this request. He ordered forty families to go with them. They did not have fifty sacks of flour to live on, and their possessions, all told, amounted to forty donkeys and forty spinning wheels. Together they went up the mountains and reached the mouth of the little river the twins called Honeystream. Sanasar said to Balthasar:

"Shall we build our fort first, or houses for these poor people?"

Balthasar answered: "We will build their houses first, and then our fort. We can't let these poor people stay out in the sun, or shiver in the cold at night."

They started building. Sanasar was so strong that in one day he dug the foundations for ten houses, and carried trees and rocks on his back, and Balthasar was just as busy. In four days the twins built forty houses and turned them over to the forty families who migrated with them. Every day they had their meals in a different house, and after the bread was baked, they hung up the owner's vat and sieve.

After the newcomers settled down the boys began to build their fort, which took more time. Sanasar went to the city and brought master builders and workers with him, who were astounded to see him carry huge rocks on his back. A hundred men together could not move these rocks. The fort was finished in a year; then they turned around and built a little church, in one day, beside a cross-stone.[8]

Sanasar said to Balthasar: "The job is done. All we need now is a name for our fort. What shall we call it?"

They asked everybody to suggest a name, but people just gaped at the fort, unable to speak. They were tongue-tied. The twins went to Blue Castle and said to the King:

"We have built our fort, it's finished, and now we have another favor to ask of you: come see it with your own eyes, and give it a name."

The King of Blue Castle was very pleased by this request. He said: "You have not forgotten me." And he arose, mounted his horse, and the lady Dzovinar and Uncle Toros also mounted their horses, and followed the twins to the new fort high in the mountains. The boys showed them around. They started out from the western gate in the morning and returned to it at sundown.

Sanasar said: "May the King live long, we can't think up a good name for it."

The King gazed around, flabbergasted by what he saw. He said: "Boys, may God preserve your home, how can you expect me to find a name for this . . . mountain on top of a mountain? All these awesome rocks, placed on top of one another. How could you do it? What superhuman strength! This is not a fort, this is not a town, this looks like the wrath of God."

"Grandfather, don't say another word," said Sanasar. "You named it. The Wrath-of-God."

That is how it came to be called the Wrath-of-God, or Sassoun.[9]

The lady Dzovinar advised her sons to ask for other territories from the King. "Tell him you want Dzovasar, Marouta's river, Chapakchour and Khout. If he swears by 'Bread and wine, the living God,'[10] he will give them," she said.

Sanasar said to the King: "One more favor."

"Sons," said the King, "whatever you want, besides my soul, Bread and wine, the living God, I will give it."

The twins said: "Give us Dzovasar, Marouta's river, Chapakchour and Khout."

The King said: "Sons, they are yours."

The King mounted his horse and returned to Blue Castle, where he died. The lady Dzovinar and Uncle Toros stayed in Sassoun with the twins. Sanasar was a very powerful man and he extended the boundaries of Sassoun all the way to Moush and Seghansar, to the mouth of Eastern Euphrates; and one day, while hunting, he rode all the way to the bridge over the Bat-

man river that flows into the Tigris, all the way to Egypt. Sanasar became such a mighty pahlevan that the whole world heard
of his exploits. Many people said:

"Brother, why should we stay here and let thieves and rob-
bers come take everything we have? By God, we will go to
Sassoun, where we don't have to pay taxes and we can keep what
we earn. A couple of mighty pahlevans like Sanasar and Balthasar will protect us in Sassoun."

And one by one or in small groups people moved to Sassoun.
Its population grew, it became a big town.

NOTES

[1] Padishah. From Persian: generally means king; particularly the sov-
ereign of Persia and Turkey. In some variants the Caliph of Baghdad is
Persian.

[2] Vardapet: teacher or doctor of the church; a member of an order of
celibate preachers corresponding to the archimandrite in the Greek church,
whose badge of office is a pectoral cross and a pastoral-staff like that of
Byzantine bishops.

[3] Tonir: a well-like oven, in which bread is baked and meals are cooked.
This used to be fairly common practice in Armenia up to recent times. The
baking of bread, as the staff of life, has sacred implications. The tonir may
replace the church for the baptismal ceremony.

[4] Pahlevan. From Persian: strongman, hero, wrestler, champion.

[5] St. Karapet: the Herald, or John the Baptist, most popular saint in
Armenia.

[6] Mamik: diminutive of mam, or mother, grandmother.

[7] The dragon is symbolic of the landlord or tyrant who controls the
waters people need for irrigating their land and who must have his pound
of flesh. A recurrent thematic element in world forlklore.

[8] Cross-stone: a decorative cross is carved on the slab. Some of these
ancient cross-stones in churches and cemeteries are very beautiful.

[9] Sassoun: pronounced Sassoon, is Sassoum in some variants (one *s* in
Armenian), and is popularly supposed to be derived from *tsasoum*, the
wrath of God or a punishment from heaven. There are other popular ex-
planations for the origin and meaning of this name. In all proper nouns
ou pronounced as in French, or as in *rouge, routine*.

[10] The living God: in contrast to the dead or inanimate idols of pagans.

THE MARRIAGES OF SANASAR & BALTHASAR

GOLDEN-HAIR-OF-FORTY-BRAIDS, daughter of the King of Copper City in Chin-ma-chin,[1] saw Sanasar in her dreams and fell in love with him.

She took two clay pitchers and filled one with water, leaving the other empty. She closed the mouth of each pitcher with an apple, and wrote him a letter, enclosing her picture, drawn by a court artist. This is what she wrote:

"Golden-Hair-of-Forty-Braids sends affectionate greetings to Sanasar in Sassoun. Many greetings to Sanasar and Balthasar. Sanasar, I am the daughter of the King of Copper City. My heart is clean and virgin-pure like this empty pitcher. My head is filled to the brim like this full pitcher. I am loaded with God's grace. Forty champion strongmen from forty kingdoms want to marry me, but I have not said yes to any of them. I saw you in my dreams and I want to marry you. You please me very much. I will be waiting for you."

She called two girl messengers and tied the pitchers on their backs. She said: "Take them to Sassoun and deliver them to

Sanasar. Drop them on his bed through the roof window. If he is such a brave man, let him come and take me. Be sure you don't deliver them to Balthasar."

These girls, like Golden-Hair-of-Forty-Braids, were skilled in magic arts, and they put on feathers and became a couple of white doves. They flew to Sassoun and alighted on the roof of the main house. They looked down through an opening in the roof and saw a young man sleeping in his bed. His face was flushed with perspiration and he was so handsome he seemed to say to the sun: "Stand back, and let me come out and shine in your stead." Two candles were burning at the head of his bed, and two candles at the foot of his bed. One of these flying messengers said: "Sister, let's look down through that other opening in the roof. This may not be Sanasar."

They saw another young man sleeping in his clothes and he was so flushed, so red-cheeked, that he was ten times better-looking, and the sister dove said: "He must be Sanasar. We will give the letter to him."

The other messenger said: "I don't know, sister, I am not sure who is Sanasar, I am confused. Let's be certain we give her letter to the right man."

Who is Sanasar, who is Balthasar? They couldn't tell. They flew back to the first window and dropped them on Balthasar's bed, and left the letter on his pillow.

Balthasar found it in the morning while he was putting on his clothes and he opened and read it. "What does this mean?" he said. "She greets Sanasar twice, and me only once. I don't understand this. 'Come and take me, I will be waiting for you.' Why, my brother wants a wife and does not tell me about it." He saw the picture in the letter and went crazy over it.

He was deeply wounded. "What kind of brother is he? We did everything together, and now this secret correspondence. I had better get on my horse and go away, get lost in some other country, seek my fortune elsewhere. I don't want to live here anymore."

The church bells rang for matins. Balthasar stayed in his room. Father Melchizedek said to Sanasar: "Son, I don't see Balthasar, go tell him it's time to glorify God. Or has the devil deceived him this morning?"

Sanasar went and knocked on Balthasar's door. Come to matins. We are waiting for you."

Balthasar said in an angry voice: "Go away. Leave me alone. I don't care to pray with you. You aren't my brother any more."

Sanasar was puzzled and did not know why his brother was so angry with him. He returned to church and told Father Melchizedek to start the service, Balthasar was not coming for matins.

Balthasar did not show up for breakfast, either. His mother went to his room and asked him: "Are you sick? Why aren't you coming for breakfast?"

"Mother, just read this." He gave her the letter, and she read it.

"How can I sit down and have breakfast with him as if nothing has happened? I thought Sanasar and I had no secrets from each other. He has been looking for a wife but tells me nothing about it. It seems I am not worth bothering with. I am so angry I could kill him."

She said: "Son, I know nothing about this Golden-Hair-of-Forty-Braids. This is news to me. He hasn't told me anything."

She took the letter and gave it to Sanasar. "Read it. It's for you."

Sanasar read: "Golden-Hair-of-Forty-Braids sends affectionate greetings to Sanasar in Sassoun. Many greetings to Sanasar and Balthasar. Sanasar, I am the daughter of the King of Copper City. My heart is clean and virgin-pure like this empty pitcher. My head is filled to the brim like this full pitcher. I am loaded with God's grace. Forty champion strongmen from forty kingdoms want to marry me, but I have not said yes to any of them. I saw you in my dreams and I want to marry you. You please me very much. I will be waiting for you."

He said to his mother: "I don't know her. I am surprised, as you are. I have no idea who she is."

"Your brother is terribly upset about it."

"Why blame me? I have no secrets from my brother."

The younger brother had a crazy streak in him, and people called him Mad Balthasar. He said: "Let us fight. Either you kill me, or I kill you."

Sanasar said: "What for?"

"Why does the daughter of the King of Copper City greet you twice in her letter and has only one greeting for me?"

"Brother, why blame me for it? That's the way she has it. What can I do?"

"No, we have to fight."

"Fight for an empty greeting like that?"

Balthasar said: "You wrote to her secretly. Why didn't you tell me?"

Sanasar said: "Brother, God is my witness I have not written to her."

Balthasar said: "Meet me at the arena."

Sanasar couldn't talk him out of it. "I will play with him a little until his anger subsides," he said to himself.

The two brothers mounted their horses and rode out to the arena. They dismounted, and began wrestling. They fought until noon. Their mother said: "They didn't come home, where are they?" She stepped out of the house. The rocks echoed with their shouts and the earth shook under their feet. She went to the arena herself and watched them fight, beating her knees and crying. Neither was able to throw the other down. She saw that Sanasar wasn't serious about it, he was joking, but Balthasar fought with all his heart. She saw him getting weaker. They fought until dark, and in the evening they came home. Balthasar said on their way: "We will continue fighting tomorrow."

They slept until morning, ate their breakfast, and taking their maces and shields jumped on their horses and rode back to the arena, their mother now going with them. She sat there and wept, cursing the sorceress in Copper City.

"She is the cause of it all. My two boys are trying to kill each other because of her."

The twins fought on horseback, striking each other with their maces, but Sanasar, whose heart was clean and pure, was merely going through the motions, while Balthasar intended to kill him, so that he could marry Golden-Hair-of-Forty-Braids himself. Sanasar decided to strike him just once, not too hard but hard enough to shake him, to see how strong his brother really was.

Balthasar held up his shield to stop his brother's mace, and fell off his horse.

Sanasar cried: "I didn't mean to hit him so hard. I didn't know the strength of my arm. I killed my brother."

He dismounted, and ran to his brother, and their mother came running from the other side of the arena, and both were crying. They saw that Balthasar wasn't dead. He lay on the ground unconscious. Sanasar rubbed his brother's heart and he stroked his abdomen. Sanasar carried him home on his back, and on their way, the picture of Golden-Hair-of-Forty-Braids dropped from Balthasar's pocket. Sanasar picked it up.

They put Balthasar to bed. Sanasar sat up all night crying. Balthasar was conscious the next morning. Sanasar sat by his brother's bedside and asked him: "Brother, what happened?"

Balthasar said: "Your mace struck me in the leg and knocked me out."

Sanasar said: "Brother, it's foolish of us to fight over a letter. If she pleases you so much, go marry her yourself. She is yours."

Balthasar said: "Brother, I didn't know you are much stronger than I am. Come, let us reconcile, and be good brothers again. You are braver than I am. From now on I am your little brother, I shall do what you tell me, you are the headman in our home. You go to Copper City and bring her here for yourself. She belongs to you."

Sanasar said: "No, I will not do that. You go get her yourself."

Balthasar said: "I am telling you she is yours. She has heard about us and wrote a letter, and if you don't go and claim the bride, people will say we couldn't do it, and we couldn't bring the bride home, and we shall lose face. It would be a shameful thing for a couple of strongmen like us."

Sanasar went to his mother, the lady Dzovinar, and said:

"O mother, have my clothes ready and make the necessary preparations. That letter was for me, and I cannot ignore it, as Balthasar says. I am going to Copper City to meet Golden-Hair-of-Forty-Braids."

The lady Dzovinar said: "Son, don't go. We managed to get out of Baghdad alive, we have had enough troubles, and I see no reason why you should go to the end of the world to find a wife."

Sanasar said: "I have to go. She is waiting. I can't turn down the daughter of a king. True, I have not seen her yet, but I think I am already in love with her. It's time I settled down and had a few children of my own."

Sanasar wore his best clothes and slung on his arms. He kissed his mother goodbye, and he and his brother asked each other's forgiveness for wrongs done in the past, and exchanged their rings. He stepped into the stirrup, swung over and settled himself in the silver saddle inlaid with mother-of-pearl, and called out to his brother from the road:

"Balthasar, may I die for your soul, don't go away while I am in Copper City. Stay with mother. I may need you. Keep your eye on the ring. I hope to be back in three days."

His fiery horse ran like a whirlwind and covered a distance of forty days in one day. He pulled up when he came to a crossroads and saw an old man sitting by the roadside.

"Good day to you, papik."[2]

"God's day to you, Sanasar. I want to talk to you."

"How do you know I am Sanasar?"

"I am God's angel, and besides, who wouldn't know the conqueror of the Caliph of Baghdad?"

"What are you doing here, papik?"

"I tell people which road to take. Where are you going, Sanasar?"

"I am going to Copper City. Show me the road."

The old man said: "If you take this road, you will be a king. If you take that road, you will be a merchant. But if you take the road to Copper City you will get hurt."

"Why should I get hurt?"

"Son, Copper City is in a land of magic. The whole city is controlled by witchcraft. It is a strange place, out of this world."

"I am going even if they chop off my head. I am not turning back. Do you have any other advice to give me?"

He said: "Son, be sure you greet everybody and everything you meet on your way. Rocks, bushes, trees, animals, wild beasts — greet them all. Don't pass any of them without greeting them."

He spurred on his horse and saluted left and right, as the old man told him, and God knows how far he went until he saw a giant shepherd raise his crook and sign him to stop. He was one of the King's strongmen tending his flocks and guarding the road to Copper City, spying on travelers.

He said to Sanasar: "Hey, you bold one, green hero, where are you going in such haste?"

"To Copper City."

"Get off your horse and rest for a while. I want you to be my guest. Eat my bread and milk, and then go."

"No, I can't stop, I have to hurry."

"Nobody who passes by here can go without tasting my milk. No traveler can refuse my hospitality."

He forced Sanasar to dismount and to be his guest. He poured the milk into a wooden trough large enough for four men to bathe in and placed it before Sanasar. He gave him a big loaf of bread, and a spoon, and said: "Eat."

The King's shepherd was testing Sanasar's strength. He could tell how strong people were by their appetite, and all travelers had to take this test by order of the King of Copper City. The strong ones were allowed to pass, and the King's strongmen killed them before they could see his daughter, Golden-Hair-of-Forty-Braids.

The shepherd said: "Enjoy your food, Sanasar. I will go take a look at my flock. I will be back."

The shepherd wanted to know how many times he would have to go around his flock before Sanasar finished eating. He went around only once when he heard Sanasar calling him. He hurried back, and his knees shook when he saw the trough was empty. Sanasar said: "Thank you. I had better get going. Good-bye."

The shepherd said: "Be on your way, and good luck with Golden-Braids. No matter were you go, you need fear no man. Any man who can eat that much is bound to win."

Sanasar mounted and continued on his way to Copper City. At last he was at the city gate, and what did he see? Forty old men yellowed with age waiting at the city gate, which was closed.

"Good day to you, white-bearded, red-bearded, dark-bearded pahlevans!"

"God's day to you, young man. Tomorrow by noon you too will be in the condition you see us in now."

"Too bad, green hero, that you too fell into the trap of this cruel enchanter," said one of the old men.

"Once, not long ago, we too were young and strong like you. All of us here were real pahlevans, but now look at us," said another.

Sanasar said: "I don't understand this, old men. What happened to you? Why can't you move?"

They said: "We are bewitched. We have been helpless ever since we got here, spellbound. Tomorrow her bird will come and screech on this wall, and you will be done for. You will become an old man like us."

"Go back, forget her," they said. "No man has succeeded so far. It's a hopeless venture."

Sanasar said: "I didn't come to Copper City for that purpose. I am just a traveler on my way. What do I have to do with a King's daughter?"

Sanasar was wise. He wheeled his horse around and waited under a tree until it got dark, then he rode around the city walls looking for an open gate, but all the gates were closed. No one was allowed to enter the city without the King's permission. He whirled away to the race course and galloped around until he got his horse hot and excited, then dug in his spurs, uttering his war-cry, "Bread and wine, the living God, the Victory Cross[3] on my right arm!" leaped over the brass wall. The horse cleared it at one bound.

Sanasar found himself in a strange city indeed, and trotting along the mysterious streets located a wayside inn kept by an old white-bearded Armenian, where he put up for the night, paying three silver coins for himself, two silver coins for his fiery horse. He bought a loaf of bread from a bakery shop, ate it, and sat down at the inn to talk with the Armenian.

"Papik, tell me a bedtime story."

The innkeeper said: "I don't know any stories."

Sanasar said, cautiously: "I hear the King of this city has a daughter. What is she like?"

"Why do you ask?"

"Just curious."

"If you came with the hope of marrying her, give up that idea. So many kings and sons of kings have failed to win her hand, and no suitor has even seen her. She casts a spell on every man and can be seen only when her spell is broken, which hasn't happened so far."

"Papik, may God have mercy on the soul of your father, could you tell me the secret of her charm?"

"Son, a fiery man must be able to take a ring out of the mouth of a sea dragon — but that's only one requirement."

"Where does she live?"

The old man took him to the roof of the inn and pointed to a black castle in the distance. "That's her garden-palace. Her curtains are always drawn. Black curtains, so that no man can see her."

Sanasar said: "Papik, what's that light burning at the gate of the castle?"

"That's a golden apple placed on top of a column by the King's orders. The man who can take the ring from the mouth of the sea dragon, then snatch this golden apple, and tear loose the mace that hangs from the tower above it, can break her spell, but he still has to fight the King's strongmen before he can marry her. You think you can do it?"

"Why, I wouldn't even think of it. I am just a traveler here and I want to get out of here alive." He stretched his arms and yawned. "Well, it's time to go to bed. I have to be on my way early in the morning. Good night, papik."

"Good-night, son."

While the innkeeper was sound asleep and snoring, Sanasar got up, crossed himself, knelt three times, and said his prayers. He stepped out of his room on tip-toe, mounted his horse without making the slightest noise and was off to the black castle with the golden apple glowing over the gate. The moon was so bright that it was like daylight in Copper City. The streets were deserted. Nobody saw him racing around the public square. He dug in his spurs, and the excited horse leapt so high in the air when Sanasar reached the black castle that he snatched the golden apple from the top of the column. He rode away and came back to the castle an hour later, called the Victory Cross to his aid, dug in his spurs, and the horse jumped again. He pulled the mace off its hook in the tower, after shaking it hard, and threw it away. It landed at the other end of the city, outside the wall, and made a hole a cubit deep in the dry ground. Then he rode to the seaside. He dove into the sea with his mace, and struck the dragon on the head. The ring dropped out of its jaws. The dragon shook its tail, the sea monster was furious and created such a storm in the sea that the whole city was splashed with water and the streets were flooded as after a summer shower. Sanasar, with the ring also in his possession, raced back to the inn and quietly slipped into his room and went back to sleep.

When Sanasar awoke in the morning and peered out of his window he noticed that the windows of the black castle were wide open. He could see the naked figure of the King's daughter moving in her chambers. She shone like the sun, and her radiance lit up the whole city. Her spell was broken. Sanasar was the first man to see her naked.

The King said to his heralds: "I want to know who took the golden apple and the mace that was hanging in the tower. Find him and bring him to me, and we will cut off his head."

The heralds searched for the culprit and inquired at the inn. They said: "Old man, is there a stranger here?" The innkeeper said: "A young fellow came in last night and is sleeping in his room." At this moment Sanasar came out of his room and said to the heralds:

"I may be the stranger you are looking for. I came in last night."

They said: "Who are you?"

"A traveler from Sassoun."

"We have orders to arrest the man who took the golden apple."

"Here it is." And Sanasar took it out from under his blouse and showed it to them.

The heralds said: "You are the King's prisoner."

The innkeeper said in an angry voice: "Shut up, you fool. They will take you away and kill you."

He said: "Why should they kill me?" To the heralds he said: "Brothers, I am a stranger here, and you are free to question me."

The heralds took pity on him; he was such a fine-looking fellow. They said: "Look here, boy, we will hide you. It would be a pity for a fellow like you to appear before the King."

Sanasar asked them: "Why shouldn't I appear before the King?"

They said: "Son, the King wants us to seize the man who took the golden apple of his daughter. If he is brave enough to fight the King's men, his life will be spared. If he isn't brave, he loses his head."

Sanasar said: "King! What king? I recognize only one king, God. Ha, ha! I can hardly wait to fight your King. Go tell him you found the man who took the golden apple, and I am not his prisoner, I challenge him to fight me if he can. God will decide who wins. I welcome this fight with your King."

The King pondered what the heralds told him and said: "Well, he did it for my daughter after all. Bring him over. He might be the right man to marry my daughter."

Sanasar was ushered into the King's presence. He said: "I did it."

The King said: "I won't believe it until I see it with my own eyes. I want you to put the golden apple back where you took it from, in broad daylight. If you can do it, my daughter is yours. If you can't, I will chop off your head."

Sanasar mounted his horse, raced to the public square, went around a few times, came back with the golden apple in his hand, and replaced it, at one bound, on top of the column before the castle gate. He rode on, and returned an hour later.

The King said: "All right, you did it. But that was your horse's trick, not yours. I want to see you jump as high as the tower and strike it with your mace. Let us see if you can do it. If you can't, your head will roll in the dust."

Once again Sanasar came flying on his fiery horse, swinging his mace. He struck the top of the tower, and the tower crashed down.

The King said: "You seem to be a brave and skillful warrior, but the man who marries my daughter must be the champion of all champions, the strongest strongman in the world. I keep forty pahlevans in chains. Real wild ones. I will let them loose one by one, and if you can kill them all, you can take my daughter and go."

Sanasar said: "O King, I came to Copper City for three days only and I should be on my way back by tomorrow. Let them loose, all forty of them at once."

The King said: "Sanasar, if I let loose all forty of them at once they will tear you to pieces. Fight them one by one. If you win, I will give you my daughter. Otherwise, you will lose your head."

"May the King live long," said Sanasar. "I can't wait here forty days, fighting them one by one. Bring out all forty of them and either they win, or I win. That's up to God."

Released from their chains the forty strongmen of the King grunted and bellowed like forty buffaloes in a stampede as they rushed to the race-course, where Sanasar waited for them on his fiery horse, sword in hand. He cut down the first pahlevan who lunged at him, after which the others kept their distance. Sanasar wheeled around on his horse and faced them now on this side, now on that, wielding his sword and protected by his stout shield, and by nightfall he cut down ten of them, while Golden-Braids watched him from her window.

The remaining thirty thought it would be easier to get him in the dark, and they fought all night, and Sanasar killed ten more. When the sun rose in Copper City twenty pahlevans were strewn across the field. There were bodies all around him. The twenty who survived charged like demons, and Sanasar struck down ten more. His arm was getting tired, and fighting on foot, he stood among the corpses of the slain pahlevans, in a pool of blood. His feet got stuck in the bloody mud, and the ten pahlevans danced around him, afraid to get too close. Sanasar was exhausted and all he could do was to defend himself with his sword, when whom did he see but Balthasar coming to his aid from across the field on his own fiery horse, brandishing his spear and yelling, "Bread and wine, the living God, the Victory Cross on my right arm!"

Sanasar said: "Blessed is our merciful Lord, I am saved!" He shouted: "Why, is that you, Brother Balthasar?" Balthasar said: "Yeah, it's me." Sanasar said: "Help yourself, only these ten are left."

Caught between Sanasar and Balthasar these ten pahlevans took to their heels, and Balthasar killed them all. He came, pulled his brother out of the bloody mud, and they left the field together, Sanasar leaning on Balthasar. Balthasar washed him up at the fountain, he was covered all over with blood, and as he opened his eyes Sanasar asked: "What happened to those ten pahlevans?"

"I finished them off," said Balthasar.

The victorious twins went to the King's palace to claim Golden-Braids and take her away by force if necessary. On their way Balthasar said:

"I was washing my hands in the morning when I saw your ring turn black on my finger, and I knew you were in trouble. A shepherd stopped me on my way, the devil take him. He made me eat his milk and bread, knowing I was your brother. He told me he had you as a guest too, and since he went around his flock seven times before I cleaned up the trough he said you are seven times stronger than I am. And then at the city gate I met the forty old men with white beards, red beards, dark beards, yellowed by age from head to foot, including their clothing, and unable to move, bewitched by Golden-Hair-of-Forty-Braids. They thought you were dead and advised me to turn back. They heard no more noises from the race-course and thought it was all over. I couldn't clear the wall, with all the gates closed, and I had to use my mace and I tore open a hole big enough to get in with my horse."

The King said: "Sanasar, Golden-Braids lives in her own castle just outside the city, and her gate-keeper is the demon Hamdol. You may have her if you can take her."

Balthasar stayed in the city and Sanasar rode off on his horse and stopped before a white castle on a big rock. "Hey, open the gate!"

"Who are you?" said the demon Hamdol from behind the gate.

"Haven't you heard my name?"

"No, what is it?"

"I don't know my name either, but when I was a baby and my mother used to throw me up into the air she called me Hamdol's angel of death."

Hamdol opened the door a little to squeeze the visitor's hand and show him how strong he was, but to a man like Sanasar the pressure of his hand was like a flea-bite. When Sanasar pressed Hamdol's hand he squeezed his mother's milk out of his fingernails along with his blood. Hamdol fled, went to Golden-Braids.

She said: "What happened, Hamdol, why do you look so scared?"

"There is a man at the gate who calls himself Hamdol's angel of death, and he crushed my hand in his. It's a log, not a hand, that man has."

Golden-Braids said: "He must be a Daredevil of Sassoun, to be so strong."

She heard the knocking on the gate. "Open the door, or I will bring the whole castle down on your head!" Hamdol trembled with fear. Golden-Braids looked out the window and saw it was a Daredevil of Sassoun, Sanasar. She ran out, opened the gate, and said:

"Welcome, my lord."

Sanasar dismounted and they went into the castle with his arm around her neck. Hamdol disappeared. Golden-Braids said:

"Eh, Sanasar, may I die for your soul and sun, what's the good news?"

Sanasar said: "I came to take you as my woman."

Golden-Braids said: "I accept your proposal with the greatest pleasure. Where else can I find a hero like you?"

When she arose and stood in front of Sanasar, he saw that she was seven times more beautiful than in her picture and what he had dreamed of. They exchanged rings right then and there.

Golden-Braids said: "Sanasar, I am so sorry for your youth, a thousand times sorry. You are in a land of magic, you know, and I am afraid they will kill you when my people hear you came to take me away as your wife. They will not let you marry me. We have to leave here quietly under cover of darkness, or they will strike."[4]

He said: "I am not afraid of them, and we are not going to leave here at night. I will carry you off on my horse in broad daylight, and it is not necessary to argue about that at length. If you are not coming with me, let me have your final word, and I will be on my way to Sassoun, alone."

"Of course I am going with you," said Golden-Braids. "I love you with all my heart. I called you and brought you here, so that I will go with you."

As soon as she spoke these words, she was on the back of his horse, and they rode away together. Sanasar greeted the rocks and bushes and trees and wild animals they met on the road, but he failed to greet a mean black bird, which screamed loudly: "He is taking her away, Sanasar is taking away our Golden-Hair-of-Forty-Braids!"

The rocks heard this warning and passed it on to the shrubs along the road, and the shrubs passed it on to the trees, and the trees to the wild beasts, until people heard it in the city, and it passed on to other cities, and a vast multitude of people, on foot or on horseback, men and women, were in pursuit of Sanasar. The sands on the seaside, the stars in heaven, the plants on earth, could be counted, but not the people wanting to rescue Golden-Hair-of-Forty-Braids. Sanasar took her to the top of a high mountain and asked her to stay there. He drew his sword, and saying, "Bread and wine, the living God, the Victory Cross on my right arm," fell on his pursuers. Mad Balthasar came to his aid again, and all these people were caught between the twins and were mercilessly cut down until the King himself arrived upon the scene and said:

"For God's sake, Daredevils of Sassoun, stop the slaughter. Tell me what you want, and I will give it. You want my daughter? I will give her. You want a kingdom? I will give it."

The twins said: "We want your daughter."

"Take her, and clear out of here. If I let you stay in my city, you will slaughter all my subjects. I didn't know I was dealing with a couple of madmen."

The twins took Golden-Braids to the city gate where the forty strongmen were bewitched by her and could not move. Sanasar said:

"Golden-Braids, release these men."

She said: "I know they all came for me, but if I set them free you will have forty more pahlevans to fight. Let us not linger here, take me away, quick."

"No, that's impossible," said Sanasar. "I will not leave the city gate until you restore them to their former condition."

She clapped her hands and her bird flew down to the city wall and screeched. Instantly all forty strongmen became their former selves.

Sanasar said: "Hey, pahlevans. You came to Copper City for the King's daughter, who is now with me, as you can see, and I know you were willing to fight for her. Now that you are no longer under her spell and are young and strong again, hearken to my proposal: if any of you wishes to fight it out with me, I am ready. And so is my brother. She belongs to the victor."

They said: "Hey, Sanasar, Balthasar, you freed us from her spell, and we thank you for it. We have no desire to take her away from you. We are going home!"

Sanasar said: "O my brothers, you are strangers here, and so are we. Are you willing then to let me enjoy life with Golden-Hair-of-Forty-Braids?"

They said as if with one voice: "We wish you much happiness and long life together. Our felicitations, Sanasar! Her beauty is matched by your strength and courage. You fought for her, and you won."

These forty strongmen arose and saying farewell to the twins returned to their own countries. Sanasar turned to Balthasar and said: "You saved my life. Come, marry her yourself."

Balthasar said: "No, I cannot marry her. She greeted you twice in her letter, and can't you see she has eyes only for you? I think I will go to Green City and marry the girl we rescued from the dragon."

The three of them rode out of Copper City headed for Sassoun and heaven knows how far they went when they saw a blue horseman swooping down a mountain-side and coming toward them at top speed. "Hey, you thugs, murderers!" he yelled after them. "Where are you taking this fairy-faced maiden? Give her to me."

Sanasar said to his brother: "Hold my horse and I will go see what he wants."

Balthasar said: "The angel of death take you, Sanasar. You always want to fight them yourself. It's now my turn."

"All right, don't get angry."

Balthasar whirled away to meet the blue horseman, his spear at the ready.

They shouted insults to each other, jumped off their horses, and wrestled on the road. Balthasar lifted him high and flung him to the ground. He drew his sword from his side to cut off his head when the blue horseman opened her collar and shirt — and revealed her lovely breasts.

Balthasar said: "I almost killed a woman!" He drove his sword back into its scabbard and helped her rise to her feet.

She said: "Balthasar, the girl you are taking away is my sister. I was so disgusted with her witchery that I left home and disappeared seven years ago. I lived like an outlaw in the mountains, and then I went to the King of Green City. When I heard you broke her spell and were taking her to Sassoun to be Sanasar's wife, I came to be your wife. I am your betrothed. You saved me from the dragon."

All four rode on to Sassoun, and before entering the town,

the twins had a messenger inform the lady Dzovinar of their arrival with the daughters of the King of Copper City. She made preparations for the wedding: forty drummers and pipers, forty minstrels, and plenty of pomegranate wine. The whole town was invited, and the marriage of Sanasar to Golden-Braids and of Balthasar to her sister was celebrated for forty days and nights.

Later, Balthasar took his wife and went to Baghdad, to seek his fortune in other lands, and Sanasar stayed in Sassoun. Balthasar died childless and was buried in Baghdad. God gave three sons to Sanasar. The oldest, Meherr,[9] was the strongest and cleverest of the three. The second son, Vergo, was sickly and subject to colic. Colicky Vergo was his name. The youngest was Ohan, or Ohan-the-Thunder-Voiced, because his voice could be heard from seven cities, and he wrapped himself up in seven buffalo hides not to burst wide open when he shouted.

The lady Dzovinar died in Sassoun and some years later Sanasar dug his own grave, made his last confession and will, took the holy communion and died in ripe old age, a good man to the end and beloved by all. He was survived by Golden-Braids, Uncle Toros, Colicky Vergo, Ohan, and Meherr.

NOTES

[1] Chin-ma-Chin: China. As a mythical land of magic and sorcery rather than China in a geographic sense.

[2] Papik: diminutive of pap, or father, grandfather.

[3] Victory Cross: *Khach Patrazin*. Khach means cross, but the meaning of *Patrazin* is not clear. It is variously spelled, and in a few variants it is *Khach Paterazmin*, War Cross. It is worn on the arm, or may be embedded in the flesh of the arm, and has magic powers, warding off evil and guaranteeing victory in battle. Like Constantine, the warriors of Sassoun say in effect "In this I will triumph" when they shout their battle-cry. The Victory Cross is a hereditary possession like the Sword Lightning and other weapons used in battle, but it must be won by each individual champion as a reward for courage and Chrisian piety.

[4] Up to fairly recent times it was customary to carry off a bride as in war, with her male relatives in hot pursuit, and the bride pretending to be an unwilling captive of the groom. Very romantic.

GREAT MEHERR: LION OF SASSOUN

David's father Great Meherr, the son of Sanasar
David's father Great Meherr has said not to forget
To ask for God's mercy in reciting this tale.
O invoke God's mercy God's mercy on Golden-Braids!
O invoke God's mercy God's mercy on Uncle Toros!
O invoke God's mercy God's mercy on Uncle Ohan!
O invoke God's mercy God's mercy on Armaghan!
O invoke God's mercy God's mercy on Great Meherr![1]

Misra Melik, the warlike Lord of Egypt, was a man close to the Caliph of Baghdad. When he heard Sanasar was dead, Misra Melik rose and marched on Sassoun with all his forces. Sassoun paid him tribute for a few years: forty barren heifers, forty measures of gold, forty virgin maids every year.

While Sanasar's sons were still under age his widow Golden-Braids ruled in his stead. She saddled his horse, took up his arms, put on his steel boots and armor, and rode around in great style, holding his mace in her hand and his shield suspended from her back.

In one month Meherr grew as much as other children grow in a year, and when he was seven years old he was more than seven feet tall. While playing with other boys he broke their arms and legs, and Uncle Toros did not know what to do with him, he was so strong. They sent him to school, where he learned to read and write and acquired a few graces.

Meherr said one day: "My mother, I have had enough schooling. Let me go to the mountains and hunt."

She said: "You are still a child. Be patient. Wait a few years before you go hunting in the mountains."

He said: "There is no man in the house and it is time I became a man. I must get ready to fight the devs."

Golden-Braids realized it would be impossible for her to give orders to her son. She let him have a bow and practice casting a mace. He tramped in the mountains and fields, hunting all day. He had no horse and came and went on foot.

One day he could not outrun a fox and came home tired and angry. He threw down the log he carried as a walking-stick and sulked in a corner of the room.

Uncle Toros said: "What happened, boy? What are you so angry about?"

"Uncle Toros, to the devil with this kind of hunting. I ran hard all day, and I caught nothing. These wild animals are getting a little too fast for me."

Meherr grew so heavy that his feet sank in the earth.

"Boy, you must be mad to be running after wild beasts and trying to catch them with your bare hands."

"What can I do?"

His mother said: "My child, there is a Prince Gorgik in Bitlis who has many fiery horses and is a good friend of ours. Go to him and ask him to give you a horse. You need a horse for hunting."

Meherr said: "I will go to Bitlis tomorrow morning."

He got up at daybreak, put a couple of millet loaves in his pouch, pulled up a tree by its roots, swung it to his shoulder and started out for Bitlis, proud of his strength. "Bitlis where are you? Here I come!"

When he reached Bitlis children playing on the outskirts of the town crowded around him. They saw a huge fellow striding along with a tree on his shoulder and said: "What kind of man is he? Where is he going with a tree on his shoulder?"

Meherr went up to them and said: "Boys, can you show me Prince Gorgik's house?"

They said: "Come on, we will take you there."

They led him to the gate of Gorgik's house, where he put down his tree and leaned it against the wall. He walked in brusquely. He found Prince Gorgik talking with his princes in his sitting room. Meherr saluted. Prince Gorgik did not return his salute. Meherr said: "He must be Prince Gorgik." He crossed the room, took hold of the man's arm and pulled him from his seat, not too hard. Gorgik realized his arm broke in seven places. He turned to the young giant and said: "Hey, brave fellow, where are you from?"

"I am from Sassoun."

"Whose son are you, my boy?"

"Sanasar's."

"Welcome, my boy, a thousand times welcome."

The prince made a half-hearted attempt to embrace him. "Meherr, my soul, you have become a real man." He had him sit down beside him, and pretended to be his friend, seeing how strong the boy was. "Bring my boy some food," he said to his servants.

Mcherr sat down and rested, enjoyed a very good dinner. After he finished eating and drinking Gorgik asked him: "Son, what is your name?"

"Meherr."

"Meherr, my boy, what brought you here?"

"Uncle Gorgik," Meherr said, "I have grown so big and heavy that I cannot run after the wild beasts as I used to when I hunt in the mountains. They escape me. I came to ask you to give me a good horse, so that I can hunt on horseback. But I don't want to waste much time in Bitlis."

Gorgik said: "Meherr my soul, I will give you my life. Is that all you want, just a horse? You can have ten horses. I have forty in my stable."

He called his groom. "Take my boy to the stable and show him our horses. Let him have the one he likes."

Meherr walked into the stable with the groom and what did

he see? Twenty horses tied in their stalls on one side, twenty horses on the other side, the saddles of all forty gleaming with silver and mother-of-pearl, bits of steel between their jaws.

The groom said: "Meherr my soul, take the one your heart desires. It is yours."

Meherr moved along the stalls and pressed down the backs of all these mighty horses. Their backs caved in, their bellies sank to the ground. Not a single horse stood firm when Meherr pressed its back. He turned to the groom and said: "There isn't a horse here I can use. They are all worthless."

As Meherr was coming out of the stable he saw a shaggy, fat colt, a two-year-old that was not tied in a stall and was still unbroken. He said in his mind: "There is nothing for me here. I will give this colt a punch, break him in two, and go." As he punched him in the stomach the colt sprang up to the ceiling and kicked so hard as he flew over ten horses that Meherr would have landed in Sassoun if the colt had kicked him. Fire blazed out of the wall where the hooves of the colt struck.

"Holy Cross!" Meherr said. "The horse to carry me on his back or to throw me off is this colt. I know my strength. I punched him hard enough to kill him. I will ask Prince Gorgik to give me this colt. I will take nothing else. If he says no, I will not waste any more time here."

He returned to the prince's sitting room. Gorgik asked him: "Meherr my soul, which horse did you like best?"

"Prince Gorgik, you can keep your horses, I don't want any of them. But I will take the shaggy colt running loose in the stable."

Gorgik said: "Meherr my boy, I am after all Prince Gorgik, and I will be ashamed to give you that ugly colt. What will people say? Sanasar's son come to me for a horse, and I would not give him one of my beautiful war horses as a gift, but an unbroken colt."

Meherr said: "No, Uncle Gorgik, I just want that colt. If you don't want to give him to me, I am going home."

"My boy, you know best. I cannot force you to take a horse you don't want. Take the colt then."

The groom threw a bridle over the colt's head and led him out of the stable. He handed the bridle to Meherr. Meherr tried to pull the colt after him, but the colt would not move. He asked for a rope. They brought him one. He tied the feet of the two-year-old securely together and stuck his tree-trunk between the legs and swung him over his shoulder.

"Goodbye, Uncle Gorgik, may God preserve your home and keep you prosperous."

"Where are you, Sassoun, here I come!" On his way back Meherr passed again through Bitlis. People in this city are devils. The urchins ran after him. They ridiculed him and laughed at him. "Look at this man carrying a horse on his back!" Meherr ignored their jeers, and strode on to Sassoun.

Uncle Toros saw him coming with a colt on his shoulder and said: "Boy, is this shaggy colt all you could get from Gorgik? Couldn't he give you a real horse?"

Meherr said: "Uncle Toros, you were right. Prince Gorgik has forty horses in his stable as you told me, but when I pressed their backs down, their bellies struck the floor. I did not find a single horse that is of any use to me. But when I took a punch at this colt he sprang up to the ceiling and gave a couple of kicks as he flew over ten horses that brought fire out of the wall."

His uncle said thoughtfully: "That is a fiery colt then. Give him to me. I will keep him for you. I will break him. You can ride him after three months."

Uncle Toros was a blacksmith who shoed horses, and a veterinarian. He kept the colt in his place for three months, and then gave him back to Meherr, ready to ride. Uncle Toros named him Colt Jalali.[2]

Once Meherr became a horseman he turned the town upside down. He killed so much game that he fed the poor of Sassoun for seven years.

When Meherr was fifteen there was a famine and the people of Sassoun crowded at his door, asking for bread. "For God's sake do something, we will starve to death."

Meherr said: "I cannot understand why we should have a famine. I will go talk to my uncle about this. I am puzzled."

He went over to his uncle's house and said: "Our people are starving, there is no bread. Can't you do something to save them?"

Uncle Toros said: "Son, what can I do? Your father's store-rooms are empty."

"Why? Did hail destroy our crops? Did the wind carry off the grain from threshing floors? Or is it because we had a drought?"

"Son, in our country we do not have much land for the plow. We grow few crops. We keep goats, cattle, mules, donkeys. We get most of our grain from Damascus and Aleppo. But a lion[3] will not let us plow our fields and has barred the road to Damascus."

Meherr said: "A lion? What do you mean by a lion?"

"The lion is the king of beasts and eats men."

"I am going against that lion tomorrow morning."

"Son, don't go, he will eat you up."

Meherr ignored his warnings and mounting his Colt Jalali went out against the lion. All the horsemen in the town, his soldiers, went with him. Meherr dismounted. When the lion saw a man coming against him he leapt out of his lair and advanced with a roar toward Meherr, raising clouds of dust with his tail. Meherr asked his soldiers: "What's that?"

"That's the lion," they said.

"I warn you if anybody strikes this lion with his sword I will turn around and kill him. The lion too is one of God's creatures and was born of a mother, as I was. I shall drop my sword and shield and fight with my bare hands."

The other men fell back and kept at a safe distance as Meherr grappled with the lion, alone against the beast. He cried out, "Bread and wine, the living God," and seizing the lion by its jaws tore him in two. He threw one half of the beast to one side of the road, the other half to the other side. His soldiers now pressed around him, not believing their eyes, and one of them rode off to take the good news to Golden-Braids. "Light to thine eye, Meherr killed the lion."

From then on he became known as Lion-tearing Meherr. He rode back to Sassoun and people thronged at his door and hailed him as their new headman: "We want you to govern Sassoun," they said.

When they made him their new governor Golden-Hair-of-Forty-Braids gave him his father's Sword Lightning, his father's clothes and armor. And riding his Colt Jalali Meherr toured his father's lands, and the enemies of Sassoun bowed their heads low before him.

Some time passed and one day Uncle Toros and princely men gathered in Golden-Braids' room and said: "Don't you think it is time for Sanasar's son to marry?" They consulted with her, and the next morning Uncle Toros, Uncle Ohan and their warriors mounted their horses and rode out to King Melkon's city. King Melkon asked them: "What is the purpose of your visit?"

Uncle Toros said: "King, we have come on some important business. Can you find us a good girl? It does not matter whether she is a city girl or country girl as long as she will make a good decent wife for Meherr."

Melkon said: "Come on, let us go to Manzikert and ask Tevatoros to give his daughter Armaghan for Meherr."

King Melkon and his vizier, Uncle Toros and the warriors from Sassoun, rode on to Fort Manzikert[4] and halted at Tevatoros' door. They asked: "Is Tevatoros in?"

They were told, "Tevatoros has gone to Van."

They had a light breakfast and rode on to Van. "Is Tevatoros here?" they asked, and they were told, "No, he just laid the foundation of the fortress, ate his breakfast and went on to Erzurum."

They rode out to Erzurum and asked: "Is Tevatoros here?" And they were told, "He just laid the foundation of the fortress, ate his lunch and went to Kars."

They rode on to Kars and asked: "Is Tevatoros here?" They were told, "He just laid the foundation of the fortress, ate his dinner and went to Manzikert."

They came back to Manzikert, and sent a mounted messenger ahead of them to inform Tevatoros of their arrival in his city and to tell him that King Melkon, Uncle Toros, Ohan and their men wanted to be his guests.

Tevatoros in his turn sent out a mounted messenger to invite them all to his home, and then rode out to receive them and to bring them personally to his palace. He gave them a banquet and had the princes and their men sit according to their ranks. After they had finished eating and drinking and the tables were cleared away Tevatoros asked King Melkon: "Well, King, tell me what business brought you here."

"Marriage business." And the other men said: "We want our boy Meherr to marry your daughter Armaghan. Will you give her?"

Tevatoros asked them: "Whose son is Meherr?"

They said: "Sanasar's."

He said. "Melkon, Uncle Toros, Ohan, I am glad you came, and you can have my daughter as a gift from me, but it is seven years now that Armaghan is a captive of the White Dev, lord of Akhlat. If she were freed, she would be Meherr's."

At that time the White Dev was king of Akhlat. He heard that Meherr's fame was spreading around the world. He said: "Sooner or later Meherr will want to take Akhlat away from me." The White Dev rose and wrote him a letter, which he gave to his strongman Kami to deliver to Meherr.

When Kami reached Sassoun Meherr was hunting in the

mountains. Kami suddenly appeared before him and said: "Oho
. . . greetings, greetings, Meherr. Have you become so great and
mighty that you come to the mountains to hunt? Know that the
White Dev challenges you." He handed him the letter. Meherr
read it and said: "Good, I am coming."

The demon who brought him the message said: "Meherr, I
have a favor to ask of you. We want you to know that we do
not love the White Dev. We want you to come and kill him,
free us from his clutches. Would you promise to do it?"

Meherr said: "I promise. I never go back on a promise. We
strongmen of Sassoun never tell a lie."

Meherr went home, kissed his mother's hand and said: "The
White Dev sent me a challenge."

Golden-Hair-of-Forty-Braids said: "You are still a child, how
can you fight the White Dev? Of all kings he is the strongest,
and no sword has any effect on him. Meherr, be a little patient,
wait until you grow up before you fight the White Dev."

"My mother, it is good to be patient, but I have already accepted his challenge. I am going."

Golden-Hair-of-Forty-Braids said: "Very well then, go, but
take my advice and wear Sanasar's armor, and put on his steel
boots, and his helmet, and have his bow and arrows and his
shield on your back, and his mace in your hand, and gird on his
Sword Lightning, and mount the Colt Jalali before you leave
Sassoun."

Meherr did as his mother told him and glittering in his father's arms and armor jumped on his Colt and rode off toward
Akhlat.

He reached the summer resort of the White Dev, high up in
the grasslands. It was spring and the mountain meadows bloomed
with every kind of wild flower. The White Dev was enjoying
himself.

It was a steep climb to his mountain stronghold and Meherr
became thirsty on the way. He rode up and down the rocky

gorges looking for water and saw two devs of gigantic stature filling a buffalo skin at a spring. Meherr greeted them and said: "'Will you let me drink a little water? I am parched." The two demons said: "No one besides the White Dev can drink from this spring."

Meherr said: "Brother, all I am asking for is a little water, and I will be on my way."

They said: "No, no, the White Dev made us swear an oath to guard this spring and if a stranger comes along to let him know." They were his spies.

Meherr lost his patience. He seized one of the devs and killed him on the spot, and wounded the other, who fled. Meherr drank all the water he wanted and then went after the wounded demon, who left a track of blood behind him as he disappeared in the mountains. Following this track of blood, Meherr came to a cave in a craggy wilderness, and saw flames pouring out of the cave. He saw a fairy-faced maiden of indescribable beauty tied to a tree at the entrance of the cave, dressing the demon's wound. Meherr seized him, tied his hands and feet, and put him away under a rock. He cut the bonds of the lovely maiden and set her free. She dazzled him like sunflare. As she rose to her feet and stood before him she went out of her mind: she had never seen such a bold handsome hero. She said with joy in her heart: "Hey, you fearless man, the wildfowl with its wings, the snake on its belly, can never come here, how did you come?"

"If that is so, how do you happen to be here yourself?" Meherr said.

She heaved a deep sigh. "Don't ask me. For seven years I have been suffering at the hands of the White Dev. This lawless monster raided our country. He kidnaped me while I was strolling in our garden and brought me here before I could cry for help. He wanted to make me his wife. With God's help I have protected my virtue and I am a virgin to this day.

"I want you to know," she added, "that I once saw a dream,

and I was told in my dream that a young warrior named Meherr would kill the White Dev and free me from his clutches."

"Where is the White Dev now?" Meherr asked, without revealing his identity.

She said: "He has gone to the Black Mountain on a ten day pilgrimage and will return today. His power lies in a black bull. He goes around the world riding his black bull and causes such havoc and ruin that no one dares challenge him. Only the man who slays the black bull can overcome the White Dev."

Meherr said nothing more. He leaped on his horse and went to the Black Mountain. A black bull came out of a marsh and charged.

Meherr said his prayer, drew his Sword Lightning and plunged it into the belly of the black bull and killed him. He wheeled his horse around and rode back to the cave. He waited near the entrance.

The White Dev was back by now, enjoying a feast. He had an eye on the road and expected his two demons to bring him water, but there was no sign of them, and he said: "They have met some powerful man." He rose quickly to his feet and mounted his horse and rode out to the spring. As he was coming out of the cave, he saw a mountain of a man seated on the grass with his fiery horse grazing beside him.

The White Dev called out to this stranger in his thundering voice: "Hey, earthborn,[5] the wildfowl with its wings, the snake on its belly, can never come here, how dare you?"

"You called me and I came. I am Meherr. Let us fight."

As the White Dev heard these words spoken by Meherr he shuddered. His hands and knees grew weak. He broke into a smile and said: "So it is you, Meherr? Welcome, my friend. Come, let us go to my tent and feast until morning. We can fight tomorrow. God will make either you or me victorious."

"No," said Meherr, "our forefathers have advised us to strike as soon as we encounter the enemy."

The White Dev and Great Meherr fought on horseback for

three days and nights, and the battle sounded like thunder in clear weather. Meherr dug his fingers deep into the demon's body, as though it were made of dough. After three days of furious fighting Meherr killed the White Dev, cut off his head and flung it to the ground. He flew off to Sassoun with Armaghan on the back of his horse.

He reached Sassoun in the evening, just when Uncle Toros, Uncle Ohan and their warriors got back from Manzikert. They sent word to Tevatoros that Meherr freed his daughter. Tevatoros and his princes mounted their horses and came to Sassoun for the wedding. The fiery Armaghan and Meherr were married, and for seven days and nights people drank pomegranate wine and feasted and made merry. After the wedding Tevatoros and his princes went home.

The news that Meherr killed the White Dev reached Akhlat, and the people of Akhlat rejoiced in his victory. They invited him to their city. All the demons in Akhlat rose against Meherr and would not let him enter the city. Meherr drew his Sword Lightning and fell upon them. He killed them all, and returned to Sassoun king of Akhlat.⁶

Misra Melik was still living. The Lord of Egypt was in a rage when he heard of Meherr's growing power and fame. Was not Sassoun tributary to Egypt? Meherr knew nothing about it and did not send him the yearly tribute Melik imposed on Sassoun. "In all the wide world is there a mightier king than I am?" Misra Melik boasted in his assembly. Up stood a man from Sassoun. "Misra Melik, I will answer your question. Meherr is stronger than you are."

The King roared out: "Go to Sassoun and tell Meherr to get ready to fight me. We shall see who is stronger."

Melik's pahlevans came to Sassoun and said to Meherr: "The King challenges you."

Meherr said: "He wants to fight me? I am ready."

Uncle Toros said: "Meherr, you became a great man and you

have a good head on your shoulders. But you are not big enough to fight Misra Melik. Mount your horse and go to Egypt. Meet Misra Melik and soften his heart. Ask him to reduce our taxes. We are too poor to pay such heavy taxes. Let us settle this dispute without war."

Meherr said: "May God preserve your home, Uncle Toros. You don't mean to say we owe him any *taxes?*"

Meherr mounted his Colt Jalali and raced to the frontier at full speed, eager for combat with the King, who waited for him on his charger. Shining in all his armor like a great fortress on horseback, Meherr came storming across the plain, and when he reached the frontier he saluted the King. Misra Melik was too awed to return his salute. He said in his mind: "Is it possible for such a man to exist in this world?" He commanded his men: "Hold his horse." They held the horse and Meherr dismounted.

Misra Melik asked him: "Where are you from, you bold one?"

Meherr said: "I am from Sassoun, Sanasar's son."

"Oho," said Misra Melik, "so you live on my land. Are you Meherr?"

"I am Meherr."

"Did you come to fight me? Why don't you pay your taxes? Sassoun is part of my kingdom. We will strike tomorrow morning."

Meherr said: "We will strike."

In the morning, Sassoun's Meherr stood up against the King of Egypt, and they began to fight in single combat. The hooves of their horses plowed up the earth as they cast their maces, each mace weighing three hundred liters. They fought in close quarters, clubbing each other; they broke away, and charged again. Some said: "It is thunder and lightning." Others said: "The mountains are shaking and crumbling in an earthquake." The world shook from the dreadful clamor of this combat. They fought for three days and nights, and both stayed on their horses and neither man could knock off the other. Meherr was mighty.

Misra Melik was crafty. And seeing what an invincible strongman he had against him and they were evenly matched Misra
Melik called out:

"Meherr of Sassoun, we fought enough, come let us make a
pact. I used to say that I am the strongest man in the world,
but I see now that we cannot defeat each other. You pay me no
more tribute and taxes. You can keep what you owe me. All
the lands of Sassoun belong to you. Go back, eat, drink, and enjoy life. I ask for only one thing in return: that we support each
other in time of war."

He said further: "If I die first, you take care of my wife and
children. And I will take care of your wife and children if you
die before me. Our children will not be orphans."

They cut their fingers, mixed their blood, sucked it, and
vowed to be blood brothers. Misra Melik did not make this pact
with a clean heart. He was afraid of Meherr. He was not sincere.

Meherr took to the road again and came back to Sassoun.
Uncle Toros was waiting for him at his door. They exchanged
greetings and Uncle Toros asked: "Meherr, my lad, did you reduce our taxes?"

Meherr said: "Uncle Toros, what do you think? Misra Melik
is a good man. He told me we owe him nothing. He said the
lands of Sassoun belong to us. And do you know what, Uncle
Toros? Melik and I became blood brothers."

Meanwhile, back in his palace, Misra Melik said to his beautiful young wife, Ismil Khatoun:[7] "Wife, without a child by Meherr, and without his stallion breeding our mares, we are finished.
That man's stock will cut up our roots. There will be no more
Egypt after my death. These pahlevans who worship the Cross
will come against us in force and wipe us out to the last man.
I wish we could have him as a guest in our home and he could
spend a week with you."[8]

Meherr took such good care of Sassoun that no enemy dared
come near it. The wildfowl on its wings could not fly over

Sassoun, the snake on its belly could not crawl into Sassoun. Sassoun made great progress under Meherr.

Some time later Misra Melik died, and his wife said: "I need a man to govern the country and pacify our warring princes. Shall we send for Meherr to come and be my guest? Let him sleep with me and let me have a child by him. My man left me without an heir."

She summoned the assembly and laid her plans before the great men of Egypt. The Queen's proposal was accepted, and it was decided to invite Meherr to Egypt.

She wrote him a letter and gave it to two pahlevans to deliver it to Meherr with the muslin veil she wore on her head. "Take this to Meherr and tell him Ismil Khatoun is calling him to Egypt."

When her messengers arrived in Sassoun, Meherr was in the mountains hunting. They waited for him. He came home in the evening and the two pahlevans stood up and said: "Misra Melik died. You too are considered to be a great king. The Queen sends you this letter with her headveil."

Meherr glanced at the headveil and said: "Let me see the letter."

He read: "Come, take me. Sassoun is in your hands, let Egypt also be yours. If you do not come you will be more of a woman than I am and you should wear my veil. You made a pact with the King to take care of his wife and children after his death."

Meherr said: "Hey, pahlevans, I am not a man to break an oath. It is a pact with God. I will have a talk with my wife, and I will be in Egypt in three days."

Meherr fed the pahlevans in his home, and they returned to Egypt. When he was alone he read the letter again, and then went to Armaghan. "Wife," he said, "Ismil Khatoun has written me a letter and is calling me to Egypt. I think I will go."

Armaghan said: "Meherr, don't go. Why should you? Do you want to lay your head on her pillow and be one with her?

Has Ismil seen you that she is sending you her headveil? What does she know about you? Are you handsome, are you bad, or good, what kind of man are you? Why is she calling you to Egypt? She will deceive you. She is an Arab. You are Armenian. She is not interested in your good looks. She has heard about your strength and courage and she wants to have a child by you. We have no child of our own. Don't go, stay here, and maybe God will bless us with a child. It is an awful thing for a man of Sassoun to leave his wife and go after a slut."

He said: "If I do not go I will be a woman like her. I made a pact with Misra Melik. I have to go."

His wife said: "Don't go."

Meherr said: "I will go."

His wife said: "Don't go."

Meherr said: "I will go."

His wife said: "Meherr, I cannot force you to stay, but if you go, I swear to God that from now on you will be nothing but a father, a brother, to me and you will not share my bed for forty years."

Meherr rose and went to his mother's room. Golden-Hair-of Forty-Braids studied the stars and said: "My son, you must not go to Egypt, the stars are not favorable for this journey."

"Mother, I have to go. I have to keep my oath. I cannot break it."

He called his friends, the princes, the vardapets, to a council in his home and said to them: "Misra Melik's widow has sent me a message inviting me to Egypt. I am going. What do you say?"

Uncle Toros said: "Melik's widow is a foxy woman and will deceive you. She is no friend of ours. You stay here."

But the princes and the vardapets thought otherwise. "Meherr, if you wish to go we cannot tell you not to go. We do not want you to ignore her plea. We want you to conquer also the lands of other kingdoms. If Ismil Khatoun is calling you, why shouldn't you go? Egypt is yours."

As Meherr prepared to leave for Egypt, what did Armaghan do? She rose, took a black cover and spread it over their bed. Meherr mounted his horse. Uncle Ohan ran to him and put his arms around the neck of the Colt and begged him with tears in his eyes: "Don't go, don't go, you have been deceived by that wicked woman."

Meherr whirled his mace as if to strike his uncle down. Ohan fell in a swoon. Meherr was surprised, and jumping off his horse rubbed his uncle's heart and spoke to him tearfully. "Ohan, my dear uncle, rise up. I made my pact with God, and if I do not go I will drop dead for breaking my oath."

Ohan rose to his feet and standing upright said:

"Hoy, hoy, Meherr! If you must go as you say may the dry roads turn green before you, may the hand of the enemy never be raised against you."

Ohan kissed Meherr on the brow. Meherr mounted, spurred his horse, and accompanied by two strongmen galloped off to Egypt.

He left Sassoun in the morning and was in Egypt in the evening. The queen sat at her window, with her eyes and cheeks painted, and her long hair drawn out from under her headveil and hanging in braids. She had the roads repaired and for the distance of an hour's ride covered with costly rugs. The roads and streets were illuminated with candles and lamps. Dressed in pretty clothes, wearing her jewels and perfumed with sweet scents, Ismil was on display at her window. She wanted Meherr to come and see her in all her youthful beauty and kept an anxious eye on the road, waiting for him.

Meherr came like a great fort on horseback, glittering in Sanasar's armor. She saw him storming across the plain like a whirlwind. He pulled up under her window and saluted.

He said: "Ismil Khatoun, tell me what you have in mind."

She said: "Meherr my soul, is that the right way for a guest to speak? Get off your horse and come up to my chambers so that we can sit down and have a talk together."

"I don't know . . . I can hear you just as well from here. I made a vow to God I will not remove my feet from my stirrups until I know for sure what your intentions are."

"It has been truly said that you people of Sassoun are a stubborn lot. Hasn't your country been laid waste time and again and hasn't Sassoun had enough fire already that you come to Egypt greedy for more? Dismount, let me receive you as an honored guest. Why be in such a hurry?"

"No, no, I cannot stay. I do not know what you mean by such words."

She saw that she could not give him orders and she was afraid he would turn back. She cried out to her attendants: "May your homes be wrecked, don't we have seven-year-old wine? He is going back, quick, take him some wine."

Court attendants rushed out with seven-year-old pomegranate wine and, seated on his horse, Meherr accepted a goblet of wine and drank it down fast. He was thirsty. The wine quickly went to his head, and Ismil Khatoun commanded from her window, "Hold his horse." They held his horse and Meherr dismounted. He staggered along and Ismil Khatoun received him with great honors as he was led to her chambers upstairs.

Meherr asked again: "Why did you call me to Egypt?"

She said: "Because I need you for pacifying our country. The seven princes of Egypt do not recognize me as queen."

He said: "I am hungry. Let me eat first and we can discuss this matter later. Have these seven princes here tomorrow morning. I know how to deal with such men."

After he finished his dinner Ismil Khatoun poured more wine into his cup and said: "I sent you my headveil because I want you to sleep with me."

"Impossible! That's an unheard of thing in my country and is against our law. How can I go to bed with you when I am a Christian and you are nothing but a lawless pagan?"

She said: "Meherr, despite my youth and because of the King's advanced age he died without leaving an heir. I want you to go to bed with me, tonight, without delay. I want you to be my new husband and defend me against my enemies. My entire kingdom is yours if you will only love me. Oh Meherr, I have loved and longed for you with all my heart. Take me, please. Ismil and Egypt are yours."

"So this is what you called me for."

"Yes. And you will come to bed with me whether you like it or not, of your own will, or by force."

She hugged him and kissed him. She spoke to him sweet words of love and made him lie on her bed with her. She intoxicated him with wine and love. She honored him, flattered him, threatened him, until Meherr, weakening, and blind drunk, made love to her. They spent the night together. And meanwhile, by the queen's orders, his Colt Jalali was coupled with the mares of the royal herd. She conceived that night, and his horse impregnated the mares.

The next morning the seven princes of Egypt came to the palace and stood at the door of the assembly hall. Mcherr looked them over. "So you came?"

They drew back in fear, salaamed deeply and kissed the carpet before him seven times.

He said: "Hey, you princes, do you know who I am?"

They said: "Allah in heaven, Meherr on earth. We recognize none other."

The seven princes of Egypt approached Meherr on their knees and kissed his hand.

Meherr wanted to go back to Sassoun, but Ismil Khatoun would not let him go and kept him continuously intoxicated. Nine months, nine days, nine hours after their first night together she gave birth to a boy. She did not let him baptize her child as a Christian and the boy was named Misra Melik[9] to succeed the King who died.

It was wine that made him stay seven years with her. One day when Meherr came back from the chase he heard her singing these words as she played with the boy:

> "Melik, Melik, my darling boy
> Light of mine eyes, I love you so
> Wreck Sassoun's hearth, put out their fire
> Be Egypt's light, that's my desire."

As soon as he heard these words Meherr came to his senses. He said: "Oho, I came to put out the fire in Armenia's hearth so that the fire of Egypt will burn more brightly." He strode into the room and said: "Ismil, what kind of advice are you giving our boy? He has scarcely hatched from the egg and you are teaching him evil things. You want him to grow up so that he will put out Sassoun's fire, is that it?"

Ismil said: "Of course I like to play with my boy. He gladdens my heart. From a champion you get a champion. Some day my boy will conquer the world."

He said: "You want this boy to destroy Sassoun. You want him to ruin my nation, use his strength against us. Ismil, you are no longer my wife. I am going back to Sassoun."

She said: "Meherr, I wanted a son by you, I wanted an heir for Egypt, and now I do not care whether you stay or go. It is all the same to me. Do as you please."

This sobered him up. He said in his mind: "I have been here not for one day, but seven years. What shall I tell Armaghan and Ohan? My lawful wife told me not to come, but I did not listen to her advice. May I go blind for watering the enemy's field for seven years, keeping it green, while my own field dries up. May God punish me for putting out the light of Armenia and turning on the light of Egypt."

The new Misra Melik, Meherr's own seed, grew as much in one day as other children grow in a year. At six months of age he was hunting all day. Once Meherr saw him coming back with a wild sheep on his shoulder. On another day Melik came home with a couple of wild buffaloes under his arms. Alarmed by the prowess of his own son, and bitterly repentant, Meherr quietly went back to Sassoun.

"Light to thine eye,[10] Meherr is back," people said to Armaghan. Armaghan rose and had a mound of earth piled up behind the gate so that Meherr could not open it, and locked all the doors. Meherr came, knocked on the gate, wondering why it was closed, why he could not enter his own home. "Good evening," he said to Armaghan. "Open the gate. It is your husband Meherr."

She said: "Good evening, my father, my brother."

"Woman, don't say father, brother to me. I am still your husband."

"I swore an oath that you will be nothing but a father and a brother to me for forty years."

"I made a mistake, I am sorry, I had my fun and came back."

"I warned you you would light up Egypt's hearth and wreck Sassoun's. I told you you would have to observe the forty-day ban[11] for forty years before you can share my bed with me as my husband."

Meherr was baffled and did not know what to do. "It will be too late after forty years. By then Melik will be a fully grown up man. We cannot wait that long. Sassoun will be ruined if we do."

She stuck to her oath. He went to Uncle Toros and Uncle Ohan and explained to them what happened. They came over to his house and said: "Armaghan, remove this black cover from your bed." She removed it, and said: "I told Meherr he would be deceived by that shameless whore. He went with silver and came back with copper. I cannot break my oath."

Uncle Toros said: "Men are weak creatures when it comes to women. He was deceived, as Adam was deceived by Eve. The law is in the hands of the vardapets. We will gather the vardapets and bring them here, with a few princely men, and have them pray for the expiation of your oath."

The prelates and princes of Sassoun gathered in Meherr's home and said: "No great harm was done. He is a man after all. He went away and found himself a sweetheart, and now he is back, repentant. Armaghan, you swore that oath for how many years?"

She said: "Forty years."

The vardapets and princes performed a rite for the expiation of oaths and offered up prayers to God for the reunion of Meherr and Armaghan in holy matrimony. They said:

> "Blessed is the word of God
> And blessed are those who keep it.
> The forty years we make forty months
> The forty months we make forty weeks
> The forty weeks we make forty days
> The forty days we make forty hours."

There was a married priest of lower rank among the vardapets who was a bit off and said: "And the forty hours we make one hour."

A vardapet pronounced the benediction: "May God grant ye remission of your sins. Arise and go, be again man and wife, and may God bless you with children."

Meherr said after they were gone: "Wife, what they said is true. Will you let me into your bedroom now? Maybe God will give us a child so that the light of Armenia will keep burning."

She opened the door and let him into the bedroom. She said: "Man is the head of the house. Woman is only the feet, she has to obey her man. May God give us a child, but mark my word, Meherr, both of us will drop dead for breaking an oath. Our child will be left an orphan, abandoned on the rush-matting."

Meherr said: "Let God give us a child, and let our boy go seize Melik by his throat, and keep the light of Sassoun burning, and it does not matter if we die. The wolf cannot eat the Lord's lamb. We who live in this world — we shall die anyway. But we continue to live in our children, and the name of our family will not perish after our death."

Armaghan said: "You know best, but we are breaking an oath."

When the forty years was changed to forty months, the forty months to forty weeks, the forty weeks to forty days, the forty days to forty hours, and the forty hours were over, Armaghan let Meherr go to bed with her. And soon she was with child.

Meherr rose and went to the mountains of Sassoun and planted a splendid garden in Dzovasar[12] as a game preserve and filled it with every animal and fowl God created, and built his summer mansion there. Then he went and built a beautiful church and monastery on a rocky peak near Dzovasar, called it Marouta's High Mother of God. He brought the sick and the maimed, the blind, the lame, to the monastery, and appointed many priests and vardapets, and with that work also finished, came back to Sassoun.

Nine months, nine days, nine hours, nine minutes after reuniting with his wife she gave birth to a beautiful boy. He was christened David. Armaghan dropped dead a month after the baby was born, and a few weeks later Meherr himself was sick in bed and died. He was buried in the churchyard of Marouta's High Mother of God. Meherr ruled Sassoun for forty years, and after his death, all Sassoun was in mourning. By order of Uncle Toros all marriages were forbidden for seven years.

Golden-Hair-of-Forty-Braids mourned Meherr's death by staying in her room and locking herself up behind seven doors. She did not want to see a ray of sunlight until David grew up and took his father's place.

NOTES

[1] God's mercy, *Oghormis*, is the shorter form of "May God have mercy on his soul." This invocation is sung by the reciter at the beginning of each cycle, and he may end his recital with another *Oghormis*, but not all variants have an *Oghormis*. Some reciters consider its omission a sin, particularly reprehensible when David's story is being told.

The form varies, although the variations are slight. This particular *Oghormis* is based on the originals found in DS, vol. I, pp. 161 and 607. "God's mercy" is a short religious prologue emphasizing the basic Christian theme of the epic. The liturgy of the Church of Armenia is rich with poetic hymns asking for God's mercy, and *Ter Oghormia!* "God have mercy on us!" has been the Armenian cry through the centuries. The tone, the accent, is rather heroic in this epic — it is not a tearful supplication As in other songs we have a rhythmic pattern that is iambic, combined with the anapest, and the rising rhythm, with the stress coming last, makes the names of the characters mentioned in these short prologues, or the praise or blame, more emphatic. Generally it is praise. The negative characters are not mentioned, or if mentioned, are not excluded from God's mercy. Thus the name of Misra Melik may be among those the reciter lists for remembrance. The repetitive pattern, characteristic of Armenian folk poetry, also makes for emphasis and lends a certain native charm to these invocations, perhaps not wholly lost in English. Native ears respond to repetitive verse. In the absence of regular rhythm, in a song that is loosely metrical, as in an *Oghormis*, the repetition of words becomes a poetic device with a certain hypnotic effect on the audience, and is an aid to memory.

² Colt Jalali: a talking horse. The meaning of Jalali is not clear. May be an Arabic word, meaning marauder or robber or outlaw.

³ The lion, like the dragon, is an allegorical figure.

⁴ Manzikert: one of the great decisive battles of the world was fought here in 1071, when the Turks under Arp Aslan destroyed a Byzantine army with its Frank and German mercenaries led by Emperor Romanus, who marched into Armenia to recover the fortresses of Akhlat and Manzikert. This part of Armenia was a first line of defense against the Turks and had a Roman administration during the Turkish invasion.

⁵ Earthborn refers to common mortals. Fiery, its opposite, has connotations of the supernatural, and may also mean wondrously beautiful.

⁶ Akhlat is a town on the western shore of Lake Van and used to be the center of a rich populous district and a famous fortress.

⁷ Khatoun: means lady, princess, queen, depending on locality and period. From Tartar or East Turkish.

⁸ In some variants Meherr and Misra Melik do not fight, and Meherr sleeps with Ismil Khatoun while her husband is still alive and is entertaining Meherr at his palace. The King wants Meherr to spend a week with Ismil Khatoun in her bedchamber, so that she may have a child by the Armenian champion.

⁹ Misra Melik: "Egypt's King." Melik, spelled also Malik, is an Arabic word, and is often found in modern Armenian surnames, or used as a title of respect, indicating a kingly or princely origin. The Armenian Princes of Karabagh were called Meliks.

¹⁰ "Light to thine eye": this expression is used when congratulating someone for good news. When a child is born, or a soldier comes back

from war, or when an engagement is announced or some happy event takes place, Armenian etiquette requires congratulations and visits, and people say "Light to thine eye" on such occasions.

[11] *Kar(a)sounk,* "Forty days." After giving birth to a child a young wife is expected to stay home for forty days, and both husband and wife must refrain from marital relations during this period. David is left an orphan while his mother, or both of his parents, were in *karsounk.* "Forty days" is observed also after death, with a religious ceremony. A newly ordained priest also goes through "forty days."

[12] Dzovasar is the favorite hunting ground of the Sassoun warriors. There is a small lake at the top of this green, grassy mountain, and it derives its name from this lake.

SPLENDID DAVID: LIGHT OF SASSOUN

We turn, invoke God's mercy on
Golden-Braids—
Forty mercies.
We turn, invoke God's mercy on
Uncle Toros—
Forty mercies.
We turn, invoke God's mercy on
Uncle Ohan—
Forty mercies.
We turn, invoke God's mercy on
The old Barav—
Forty mercies.
We turn, not to praise
Chimishkik Sultana
We turn, not to praise
Misra Melik—
Do not praise them.
We turn, invoke God's mercy on

Ismil Khatoun—
Forty mercies.
We turn, invoke God's mercy on
Khandout Khatoun—
Forty mercies.
We turn, invoke God's mercy on
Splendid David—
A thousand mercies.

DAVID WAS left an orphan. Uncle Ohan said to his brother: "Vergo, who is going to keep David, you or I?" Vergo said: "You keep him. I already have a son of my own." Uncle Ohan adopted David. He said to his wife Sara: "We will get a nurse for him."

They could not find a single nurse to suckle the baby. He would not suck their milk. Ohan said: "This boy will die if we cannot feed him. What shall we do?"

Sara said: "Send him to Egypt. Let Ismil Khatoun take care of him for a few years."

"Who will take him to Egypt?"

"Meherr's horse. He knows the way."

Ohan brought the fiery horse out of the stable and groomed him well. They put the infant in a saddlebag and tied him on the back of the horse. Ohan said:

> "Colt Jalali, I beg you, please
> Not to throw him against the rocks
> Or trees and shrubs; to Egypt fly
> Take him safely to the Khatoun
> To you I trust this baby boy
> Who is our joy, light of Sassoun."

A whiplash by Ohan, and the fiery horse was off to Egypt, flying between heaven and earth. Ismil Khatoun sat at her window and watched a duststorm rising on the plain and sparks showering the sky. She said: "Must be Meherr's horse." She asked the gatekeepers to open the portals of her palace. She said: "Look at that horse!" as it came burning up the plain. They opened the gates. She saw it was his Colt Jalali. She called: "Misra Melik, there is something in that saddlebag. Bring it to me."

The horse bowed his head. Misra Melik took the bundle out of the saddlebag, and carried it to his mother. She found an infant in it, with a letter placed beside him. It was from Uncle Ohan: "My sister-in-law, our bride: This is Meherr's son David. Meherr and his wife died after their child was born and David was left an orphan. Keep him a few years, for Meherr's sake. I will take him back when he is older."

She said: "Meherr was good to me. Melik is old enough to be weaned and I still have milk in my breasts. I will keep him. Let him be Melik's brother. Melik and David can rule Egypt and together, conquer the world."

She turned to her son. "The baby for me, the horse for you."

Misra Melik shouted to his mounted warriors: "Boys, close the gates! Don't let this horse get away."

Ismil Khatoun said: "This horse can be the ruin of Egypt."

Mounted warriors surrounded the horse, but could not catch him. The Colt jumped over the wall, forty cubits high, and flew back to Sassoun. "We lost him," Melik sighed.

Uncle Ohan had his eye on the road from Egypt and saw the fiery horse racing back through the dusk, flying between heaven and earth. He went out to meet the Colt, and saw that the bundle was gone. He asked him: "Where is David? Where did you leave my beautiful baby? Did you abandon him on a mountain or rock, under a tree or bush, to be eaten by wolves and savage beasts?"

The horse said: "I did not abandon him on a mountain or rock, or leave him to be eaten by wolves and savage beasts. I delivered him safely to Ismil Khatoun, and got away before they caught me."

Ohan kissed the horse on the head and said to his men:

"Clean him up, groom him, take him back to the stable. Shovel earth behind the door and keep the stable tightly shut. We will not open it again until David comes back from Egypt. You can feed and water the horse from the roof." He pronounced a curse: "May God blight the home and the children of the person who reveals the whereabouts of this horse."

Ismil Khatoun was glad to have David with her. The infant sucked her milk for a day or two, then turned his face away from her nipples. She could not feed him for three days and nights and she was in tears, did not know what to do. She called her son. "This baby will die of hunger if we don't do something about it. He was given to us in trust and if he dies we shall be blamed for it."

He said: "Mother, his people are very stubborn and independent. He is Armenian, you are Arab. He will be a big headache for us. Don't feed him. Let him die."

"Well, we are in it now. We have to keep him alive somehow. He is your half-brother."

"He is not my brother. He will eat food from his own country. Don't you know his father had many flocks and herds and was rich in cattle and goods?"

They sent Batman's Sword and the Demon of Frankistan, Meherr's strongmen now in Misra Melik's service, to Sassoun, and they came back with forty goatskins of butter, forty goatskins of honey for David.

"See?" said Misra Melik. "I told you these infidels have plenty. Where else can you find such abundance? Their tables are loaded with sweet things to eat."

For the next three years David thrived on his native food. He grew by the day, while other, earthborn children, grew by the year. Ismil Khatoun took good care of him. David grew so strong on the butter and honey of Sassoun that he tore up the binders in his cradle and she had to use a chain to restrict his movements. The chain broke.

Misra Melik would not let him go out and play with other

children and kept him locked up in a room. David pulled the door off its hinges and walked out of the palace. He went to play with older boys and took them all to a garden nearby. He reached up, pulled down a tall poplar and said: "Come, boys, get on this tree and let us play see-saw." They climbed on the tree and he swayed them up and down, until his arm got tired and he said: "Get off, quick, I cannot hold it any more." They stayed on the tree. He let it go. As the tree snapped back they all fell to the ground. Heads, arms, legs were broken, and three of the boys died. Their bodies were displayed before the mosque and their parents came to complain to Misra Melik: "Send this orphan away, get rid of him, kill him — we don't want him here. He is a mad fool. If he stays, we will take our families and leave your kingdom."

These were the great families of Egypt and there were high officers of state and famed strongmen among them. Melik was furious. He ordered that David be kept in a dark dungeon, in solitary confinement, and appointed a master to teach him obedience. David's meals were taken to him by servants in the kitchen. One day David broke the window with a peach stone a servant left in the fruit, although it was against orders to feed him peaches without first removing the stones. David played with a sunray that came in through the broken window and chased it all over the room, not knowing what it was and unable to catch it, until the master told him it was a sunray.

David said: "If there is sun, then why do you keep me in this dark room? I want to go out and enjoy the sun."

"I will ask the King," said the master.

Misra Melik said: "Take him out for a walk."

The master showed him the sights in the city. David was curious about everything he saw and kept asking him: "What is this? What is that?" He had never seen a cow, a horse or a buffalo before. He noticed a crowd gather in the arena and said: "Let us go there." The master said: "There is nothing to see there, David. We will go this way." "No, I want to go there, where all those people are." The master would not take him to the arena until David pulled his ear. Misra Melik was playing jereed[1] with his pahlevans and princes, and David caught the King's javelin as it flew over his head and threw it back. It went over Melik's head and the King said: "Hey-hey! Who is the pahlevan who can throw my javelin that far!" The vizier sent a man to David's master with orders to remove him immediately from the arena, before the King cut off his head for catching his javelin.

One day David asked Ismil Khatoun: "Mother, where does Melik go every morning with his soldiers?"

"He goes to the arena."

"Why doesn't he take me with him? I never go anywhere. I have no one to play with."

"You stay away from your brother's games and don't you ever go near their horses. If something happens to you we shall be blamed for it."

When Melik came home in the evening his mother said: "Take David to the ball game tomorrow. Let him learn to play ball."[2]

Melik said: "David, you are still a child, wait until you grow up before you start playing with us."

David cried: "I want to go with you, I want to go with you!"

"If he stays home all day he will be fighting with the boys," Ismil Khatoun said.

"Mother, David belongs to a stubborn wilful race. He will be a curse over our heads. I don't dare take him anywhere with me because I know he will get hit by a ball or a mace, or our horses will run over him, and what will people say if he is killed? They will think I don't want to have an extra mouth to feed and I deliberately planned the murder of an orphan."

Mother and son argued about David, and Melik finally said: "All right, I will take him to the ball game tomorrow. I don't want people to say I am mean to an orphan."

Melik rose early and rode out to the field with David seated on the back of his horse. Melik ordered two of his strongmen to tie David hand and foot and keep him away from the field. It was impossible for David to follow the game from where he was sitting on top of a hill. He said to his two guards: "Pahlevans, take these ropes off me." They said: "The King commanded us to guard you during the game so that you will not go and fall under their horses."

David shook himself slightly and freed himself from the ropes. He tied both men. The guards hung from his arms and tried to hold him back as he dragged them through the streets.

"Why did you come home?" the queen asked him.

"I could see nothing," he said.

Misra Melik had another argument with his mother about David. Ismil Khatoun did not rise to greet him when Melik came home in the evening. "Why didn't you let Devid watch the ball game?" she said.

"Mother, he will not listen to me, I cannot control him, he ran away, what can I do?"

David refused to eat his dinner. She made her son promise to take him to the ball game again, and to let him sit close enough to the field to see the contest.

The next morning the city was full of horses and horsemen. Melik and his champions were to compete with their maces. Melik took David with him and let him watch the game with other spectators. "I don't care if he is killed," he said to himself. He showed his mace to David. "You see this mace? It is the heaviest mace in all Egypt. If it hits a man it will kill him on the spot. Nobody besides myself can lift this mace!"

There was not another king like Melik. He was a powerful, able ruler.

The royal band played during the game, and there were horse races and other festivities. The champions of Egypt cast their maces without hitting anybody; they were so skillful. Melik rode around before his troops, swinging his mace or whirling it over his head, and his mace weighed three hundred and sixty liters.[3] Fire blazed out of it. People pressed forward to see him cast his mace. It tore up the earth. David, sitting behind the target, on higher ground, slid down into the ditch and began measuring the sand with his tall Arab cap that had a hole in it. He counted, "One! One!" He could not count up to two.

Misra Melik yelled from across the field: "David, get out of that ditch! I am casting my mace!" He warned him three times. David pretended not to hear him.

Melik said to his strongmen: "Pahlevans, Gagan, Aslan! Go pull that boy out of the ditch."

Gagan, Aslan and five other strongmen rode up to David but could not pull him out of the ditch. It was like trying to rip up a tree by its roots. David sat there and continued to measure the sand with his cap. "One! One!"

"Strike, Melik! I am waiting!" David shouted.

(It was not in God's scheme that Armenians should ever fear Egyptians.)

Melik said: "Dust you are and to dust you return!" His mace went spinning through the air like a millstone, David thought. He shot up an arm and caught it. He weighed it in his hand. "Not heavy enough," he said. (It would have been better for David if forty liters of molten lead were poured into Melik's mace.)

The crowd gasped. Melik knitted his brows. His face fell. His men jibed him in the field. "Melik, you always said 'I am strong!' But did you see how a young boy like David caught your mace?"

David played with the King's mace and then kept it under his knee. Gagan, Aslan and other strongmen came up searching for it. David took it out from under his knee and showed it to them. He threw it up with his right hand and caught it with his left hand; he threw it up with his left hand and caught it with his right hand.

"Give it back to us."

"'Ball, ball," David said, and threw it away, killing Gagan and Aslan and five other strongmen.

The contestants in the field said: "Melik, we came here to enjoy ourselves. Why did you bring David with you when you knew he is a mad fool? What will people say when they see all these bodies? This game turned into a funeral?"

Melik drew his sword and said: "I am going to cut off his head. I will kill that orphan dog." His champions and men mature in years and wisdom fell upon him and said:

"Melik, you don't really mean to kill him."

"Have pity on an orphan."

"He is just a child. He does not realize what he does."

"May the King live long, everybody knows there isn't a pahlevan in all Egypt who can catch a mace thrown by you, let alone a child like David. This was God's work. An angel did it."

"David gets his strength from his father."

They pleaded with the boy king and did not let him kill David. David got up and ran. He did not stop until he reached home. He clung to the queen's skirts. "David, what happened?"

"Mother, Melik is coming to cut off my head."

"Why should he cut off your head?"

He told her what happened. When Melik came home he was scowling and did not speak a word. His mother said: "Why are you so silent?"

"David disgraced me before my people."

"What did he do?"

"He caught my mace, he killed my pahlevans." He turned to David, shook him by the arm and screamed: "'Why did you do it? Mother, I will kill him. I will crush the head of this viper under my heel."

She held him back. "Aren't you acting like a mad fool yourself?"

"Today, he catches my mace, tomorrow he captures my kingdom."

"Son, David can be a source of strength for you, he can be your sword, stand behind you. You will support each other when you grow up. David's father—and yours—was a great pahlevan, and tomorrow David also will be a pahlevan."

"I cannot understand it," Melik said. "Others who fall under my mace, die. No, mother, David will never support me. You took a snake to your bosom."

"Son, his mind is not formed yet. It is liquid, water. He has no comprehension of what he does."

"He is smarter than you or I."

Melik agreed to a test she proposed, and which had the approval of his vizier and other great men of Egypt. They came to the palace to watch the test. They filled a tray with red-gold pieces and another tray with red-hot charcoal and put them before David. Ismil Khatoun said: "David, take what you like." He reached for the gold, but an angel held his hand and directed it toward the glowing embers. He burned his finger, and an ember stuck to it as he carried it to his mouth, and burned his tongue also. He bawled. They took the ember out of his mouth. Ismil Khatoun took him in her arms and cried with him.

She said: "How can you kill an innocent child? He burned his tongue and he is lisping."

"You were right, that was a foolish thing to do," Melik said and walked out with his men.

From then on they called him Lisping David.

David wandered off to the armory, found the door open and went in. Melik kept his huge mace here. David picked it up and said: "What a nice thing to play with." He flung it to the ground. The noise shook the city. Misra Melik said to his vizier: "This noise was made by my mace. Go find out what happened." The vizier suspected David and ran to the armory. David dropped the mace again, causing a panic in the city. The vizier shouted from the door of the armory: "David, what are you doing here?"

David came out of the armory. "Go home to your mother before Melik gets here and chops off your head." David ran.

When Misra Melik himself reached the armory he roared out: "Vizier, who was here?"

"I don't know," the vizier lied. "The door was open when I got here."

"I am sure it was David. Nobody else besides David can lift my mace."

Melik went around looking for David. He did not find him and went home. He saw him sleeping under the trestle by the fireplace. He took the string off his bow and wanted to strangle him. His mother came in through the door and said: "Melik, what are you doing?"

"I will strangle this snake. He played with my mace in the armory."

She stood before her son and bared her bosom: "I warn you, Melik, that if you kill David the milk you sucked from my breasts would be unlawful."[4]

"Mother, this snake will be the cause of all my misfortunes."

Melik and his mother exchanged angry words about David. The vizier said: "Send him back to Sassoun. He has lived in our country long enough. Melik will kill him sooner or later if David stays here."

She called David and said: "Will you go back to your uncles?"

"Do I have uncles? Of course I will. Mother, where are my uncles?"

"They live in the city of Sassoun."

"What are their names?"

"Ohan, Vergo."

"For heaven's sake, mother, why didn't you tell me before? Give me ten pair of socks, ten pair of sandals and enough food to last me ten days, and I will go to Sassoun."

Ismil Khatoun had ten pair of socks, ten pair of sandals

and enough food to last him ten days ready for his journey. She said: "Go, my son, go to your uncles in Sassoun."

Misra Melik said: "David must pass under my sword before I let him go back to Sassoun. I am also King of Sassoun."[5]

He drew his sword and waited for David to pass under it as a sign of his submission. David said in his mind: "He does this so that I will not raise my sword against him when I grow up. If he strikes me with his sword why shouldn't I strike back with mine? A thousand Meliks cannot make me do a thing like this. I would rather pass under a woman's headveil. If he is going to kill me, let him kill me now. Let him do what he can."

The vizier tried to push him under Melik's sword. During their struggle David's little finger scratched against a flint stone and sparks blazed out of it. Melik was terrified. He said: "This happens when he is still young. What would happen when he grows up?"

He called the two strongmen, Batman's Sword and the Demon of Frankistan, and said to them: "Take David to the other side of Seven-Mountains, as far as the bridge over the Batman river, and kill him. Bring me his vest soaked in his blood, his ears,[6] and a jugful of his blood. I will dip a buffalo's horn in his blood and drink it to refresh my heart."

The two strongmen prepared for the journey. Ismil Khatoun thought they were taking David to Sassoun. David kissed her hand. "Goodbye, Mother," he said.

She kissed him on the head. "May God be with you, my boy. Come back and visit us soon. And Melik will visit you in Sassoun. I want you to be good brothers. You will forget your differences when you grow up."

David did not walk with his two escorts. He took the side-roads. He kept away from them. He was now ahead of them, now behind them. He ran up and down the hills, jumped over rocks, bushes. They did not give him any of the food Ismil Khatoun packed up for him. What did he eat? Vegetables, roots, mushrooms, or a quail or rabbit he killed with his slingshot.

When the two strongmen reached the bridgehead and sat down to eat, they called David: "Come eat with us." David came over and said: "This is the first time in five or six days that you are asking me to eat with you. You never said before, 'David, are you hungry, are you thirsty, aren't you afraid of the wild beasts?' Why do you call me now?"

They said: "David, up to this river is Misra Melik's land, but now we have reached your father's country. That's why we are calling you. Come, David, come eat with us."

"You have been eating the food Ismil Khatoun prepared for me. Now that we have reached my father's country I do not want any of your food."

David saw them getting up after they finished eating and waiting for him by the bridgehead. He approached them and said: "Why did you stop here?" They said: "We are waiting for you. Melik told us to take you safely across the river. It is a big river, and you are a small boy. We don't want you to be scared while crossing the bridge and fall into the river."

"You never said, since we left Egypt, that David is a small boy and might be scared. Go ahead. Cross the bridge. I will follow you."

"We want to protect you. You walk between us." (David did not hear them say to each other: "We will kill him here.")

Still very suspicious, he started walking across the bridge with one of the strongmen in front of him, one behind him. They grabbed him in the middle of the bridge.

"Hey, what are you trying to do, throw me into the river?" David seized them by their collars and banged their heads together until they were senseless. He hung one of them head down from one side of the bridge, hung the other head down from the other side, and said: "You don't know how to throw a man into the river. I will show you."

The strongmen said: "For the love of God don't throw us into the river. We are family men. We have wives, children."

David pulled them up, flung them to the floor of the bridge, pressed his knees hard on their chests. "Tell me the truth, or I will throw you into the river."

"David, spare us and we will tell you the truth."

"It's the truth, or your lives."

"If we hide the truth from you, how can we hide it from God?"

The Demon of Frankistan said: "That heartless, Godless Melik ordered us to kill you. He said: 'Take him to the Batman river and slay him on the bridge. Bring me his ears and a jugful of his blood. I will dip a buffalo's horn in his blood and drink it to refresh my heart.' David, I was your father's pahlevan before I was forced to enter Melik's service. I will gladly serve you, as I served your father."

Batman's Sword, an Arab, said: "We never liked Misra Melik. He threatened to cut off our heads if we disobeyed his orders. We will never go back to him."

The Demon of Frankistan said: "David, I grew up on your father's table. I ate his food. After your father died Misra Melik kept us as his prisoners. When you were an infant in the cradle we brought you the honey and the butter from Sassoun you grew on. From now on I am your servant as long as I live."

"Take us to Sassoun with you and make us your pahlevans," said Batman's Sword.

David helped them rise to their feet. They kissed his hands, his head, and he kissed them in turn. He said: "Let's go." They crossed the bridge together and when they reached the other side and set foot on Sassoun's soil Batman's Sword and the Demon of Frankistan lifted David and carried him on their shoulders.

That night, while they were on their way to Sassoun, Uncle Ohan saw David in his dream. He said: "God knows whether David is living or dead. If he is alive, he will be back. Perhaps he has already set foot on our soil. Sara, get up and make his bed."

Sara said: "Hey, old man, why don't you let me sleep."

Uncle Ohan said: "Sara, you are of foreign stock and your heart does not ache for our orphan boy. I just dreamt that the walls and tower of our city stood firm against the heathen, the lanterns glowed over the tower, the bulbul[r] sang again in our garden, which was all green. I have a feeling David is coming back."

Shepherds and drovers saw David with the two strongmen and recognized him by his clothes. He was after all a scion of the Great House of Sassoun and was dressed like a prince. "I am going to Sassoun, Sassoun is my country," he said to a peasant, and this man rushed to Uncle Ohan with the good news. "Congratulations, Uncle Ohan. Your boy David is back!"

Ohan was overjoyed with the news and informed Uncle Toros, and together they announced to the people: "The divinity gave us a new scion. Let us all go meet David and welcome him home." And people from the town and the villages, on foot or horseback, followed them down the road. Ohan saw a couple of pahlevans coming up the road, followed by a young boy who zigzagged through the millet fields. "That must be our orphan boy," Ohan said. "Twisted in his mind, twisting along. He can't walk straight."

David's sandals and socks were worn to shreds and his feet were sore and bleeding. He was hungry, thirsty. He thought: "How am I going to enter Sassoun in this condition?" He did not know where he was and had no idea that all these people were coming for him. He was confused and shied away from the crowd. He wondered why so many people wanted to shake his hand.

Ohan-the-Thunder-Voiced came forward and said: "Boy, where are you from?"

"I am from Sassoun," David said.

"This is Sassoun. I do not think I have seen you before. Do you have any relatives here?"

"My mother told me I have two uncles."

"What are their names?"

"The name of my older uncle is Vergo, and my other uncle is named Ohan."

"So it is you, David! I am Uncle Ohan." He hugged him tightly and kissed him on his forehead, crying from joy. And his other uncle did the same. "Glory be to God," Uncle Ohan said, kissing him again. "The light of Sassoun is burning again."

Everybody was happy. There were congratulations from all sides. They took him home, and there was a feast and much rejoicing at Uncle Ohan's. Princely men came to see David. All Sassounians were excited. "What a handsome boy," they said. "Such fiery good looks." "Our scion, our pigeon is back." Uncle Ohan kept praising God for his good fortune.

But David's lisping broke their hearts. They questioned him about it and he told them how it happened, he told them everything. They thanked God he was safely back in Sassoun.

After the guests were gone and David was left alone with Ohan he asked him: "Uncle Ohan, how are things with you?"

"Son, we live by the grace of God and your father's grave."

"Good, that's good," David said.

"From now on this is your home. I will keep you on my head."

The next morning Uncle Ohan knelt three times and said his prayers, thanking God for his good fortune. He went out and brought beautiful clothes for David. He dressed him up nicely and filled his pockets with nuts and raisins, gave him a handful of knucklebones, kissed him on the head and said: "David, go play with the boys in the street."

David went to play with them, and lost all of his knucklebones. The boys cheated him. He said: "Give them back." They said: "We won them. Why should we?" He slapped one of the boys, the son of a princely man, and broke his neck.

In the evening the boy's mother came to Ohan's house and complained about David. Ohan said: "I will tell him not to fight any more."

There was another fight the next day. Ten or fifteen boys

ganged up against him and tried to beat him up. David struck
back, and broke three more necks.

A crowd of angry parents gathered before Ohan's house.
The big men of the city demanded to see David.

"We don't want him in Sassoun. He will end up by killing
all of our boys. The son of a bitch is crazy."

Ohan said: "He has a fiery temper and he has become a bit
wild from eating grass and roots, but he will quiet down."
He was scared. He heard threats against David's life. He hurried
to David and said: "May God wreck your home, why do you
always fight with our boys?"

"Oh, to hell with them. They started fighting themselves
and I struck back."

"These are important people in our town. Go talk to them."

David stood in the doorway and eyed the angry mob. Some
of them had not seen him and wanted to know what he looked
like. Others wanted to kill him. As he stepped out of the house
the crowd fell back, shuddering with fear. People whispered to
one another: "Don't raise a hand against him or he will kill
us if he gets mad." They turned and went home.

Ohan said happily to himself: "He does not realize his
strength. He is the firelight of Sassoun."

Ohan sent him to school and David learned to read the Psalms
in the home of a parish priest. But David did not want to be a
burden on his uncle. He wanted to earn his own living. His mischiefs continued. The big men of the town said: "Ohan, our
children will never be safe with David on the loose. He will ruin
our town. Put him to work, keep him busy."

"What kind of work do you have in mind?" Ohan asked.

"Let him be a goatherd, just to get him out of town."

Uncle Ohan came home in the evening and said to David:
"Son, how would you like to be a goatherd? We are poor and
could use a few measures of millet."

David said: "I will be glad to work, Uncle Ohan. Maybe
somebody will give me a job, for your sake."

"David, I already have a job for you, as our goatherd. It is sweet, pleasant work, and the pay is a measure of millet and a measure of wheat per head. Do you think you could herd our flocks?"

"I will take good care of them, Uncle Ohan."

Ohan announced to the people of Sassoun: "Our goatherd this year will be my brother's son, David. Tomorrow morning bring your flocks to the city gate, and David will take them to the pasture."

Ohan's neighbors said: "The boy is barefoot. You had better get him a pair of new boots."

Ohan went to a blacksmith and had a pair of steel boots⁸ and a steel crook made for David. "These boots ought to last you seven years," he said. David was delighted with his new boots. He put them on. He took up his crook, and went to the city gate with his uncle, where the flocks gathered in the morning. When people saw David in his steel boots, holding a steel crook, they said: "Ohan, we are afraid this boy will kill our sheep and goats."

Ohan turned to his nephew. "Son, all these people are your neighbors and friends. They expect you to take good care of their flocks. Don't kill them now. Or lose them in the mountains. Bring them back safely."

"Don't worry, Uncle Ohan. I will keep them like flowers. What do you take me for, a mad fool?"

"Son, take them to the pasture on the other side of the mountain. At noon wait for me by the spring and I will bring your lunch."

David drove the flocks to the mountain pasture, turned them loose in the grass. He built a shelter for himself and lay down to rest on the hillside. He grew drowsy and fell asleep. When he awoke he jumped to his feet: his flock was gone, disappeared. He ran around looking for his goats and sheep and yelling at the top of his voice. Wild sheep and goats and hares and foxes and weasels sprang out from under rocks and bushes around him and ran in different directions, and how they ran! David raced after them, cursing the fathers of their owners. He wore them out. They stopped running. He collected these wild animals and added them to his flock, taking them for goats and sheep. He drove them all into a cave by the spring where his uncle asked him to wait for him and placed a large millstone at the mouth of the cave.

At noon Ohan brought him his lunch. He found him barefoot and his steel crook worn down to the hook at the end. David was soaked in sweat. Ohan asked. "David, what happened?"

"Oh, Uncle, the brown and white goats with glittering eyes and pointed ears tormented me. May their owners drop dead. I don't want to herd such goats. Tomorrow morning take them out of the flock. I have no trouble with our black goats. They are all right."

"Boy, what do you mean, brown goats with glittering eyes and pointed ears? We don't have such goats."

"Come, I will show you."

He led his uncle to the cave. How could Ohan remove the millstone? He peered through the hole in it and saw foxes and weasels and hares huddled together with lolling tongues, breathing hard, their eyes blazing in the dark.

"May God preserve your home, David, what have you done?"

"These are the strong and pretty goats, but very restless. I wore out my boots running after them. They really tortured me. You go in first and let the lambs out. Leave the goats to me. They are very hard to catch."

"You are small, it is easier for you to get in, I will wait outside."

David rolled the millstone to one side and crawled into the cave. He struck a wooden stick against the rocks and the weasels, foxes and hares jumped out one by one, and ran away.

David came out of the cave. "Uncle Ohan, why did you let my goats get away? What shall I tell their owners?"

He ran after them. Ohan shouted after him: "Let them go, let them go, we don't want them, they are wild beasts."

Ohan-the-Thunder-Voiced saw thunderous sparks fly from under the boy's feet.

David kept running. Ohan turned and went home. "This blackens our faces with smudge. Our David can't tell a kid from a hare." He warned his neighbors: "For God's sake don't bring your flocks to David tomorrow morning."

David drove his flock back at sundown, walking barefoot, with his steel boots hanging from the hook of his crook. "Good neighbors," he shouted, "come and get them. Who are the owners of all these goats with long tails? They are very restless. I had to beat them up to bring them back."

People said: "The boy is really mad. He has collected all these foxes and hares and mixed them with our flocks. Let us go and get them."

Uncle Ohan came over and said: "May God wreck your home, David, I told you we don't want these. Let them go. They are not sheep and goats. They are wild animals."

"I don't want them either," David said.

People came out of their houses, and each took what he wanted in addition to his own flock. They cooked the rabbits for supper. They skinned the foxes and weasels for their furs. These are still very much appreciated in Sassoun.

The princely men came to Uncle Ohan and said: "The boy is impossible. If this continues he won't leave any wild beasts in the mountains, he will collect them all and bring them to town with him. We cannot employ him as a goatherd."

They talked it over with Uncle Ohan and said: "We will make him a drover."

Ohan said: "David, my boy, goats are troublesome creatures. Herding cattle is easier and more pleasant work. Cattle aren't so restless. Tomorrow morning you start working as a drover. You can lie down in the shade and take a long nap. I will bring your lunch at noon."

His uncle brought him a new pair of steel boots and a new crook. Early the next morning they went out together and Ohan called out to his neighbors: "Hear me! My boy David will not herd goats any more, but cattle. We have made him a drover. Bring him your cattle."

David drove the herd to a mountain meadow. "If I increase their number, I increase my pay," he thought. "More cattle means more millet and wheat, and more loaves of bread."

He took his nap. When he awoke he sat bolt upright. His herd was gone. The cattle were scattered far and wide on the mountainside. He took his crook and ran shouting after them, cursing their owners. The ground shook under his feet and the rocks echoed loudly with the thunder of his steel boots. He collected all the wild beasts and added them to his herd. He brought the lion from one side, the tiger from another side. The leopard from one side, the wolf from another side. Bears from one side, boars from another side. He filled the meadow with these savage beasts. The cattle stood still, afraid to move because of all these wild beasts among them, and the wild beasts stood paralyzed in their tracks, afraid of David. When he struck, he drove them deep into the ground.

In the evening, David was back in Sassoun with a greatly augmented herd, and once again he carried his steel boots from the hook of his crook.

People bolted their doors. David stood in the town square and cried out at the top of his voice:

"Get up, good neighbors, and open your doors,
Take your cattle in, put them in their stalls.
If you had no cows I have brought you cows,
If you had no oxen I have brought you oxen,
If you had no calves I have brought you calves.
If you gave me one I have made it two,
If you gave me two I have made it ten,
If you gave me ten you get twenty back,

If you gave me twenty you get forty head
Of the sleekest cattle you ever had."
Nobody dared come out of his house. It broke David's heart.
"May you all go to Gehenna! Such a life. You try to be good
to people and this is what you get in return." He pulled his
sheepskin cape over his head, lay down and went to sleep in the
town square.

"We shall lose our herds," princely men said to Uncle Ohan.
"Your boy is ruining our town. The angel of death take him,
can't you see he is mad? Our women and children are afraid
to go out into the streets with all these wolves and bears, all
these savage beasts roaming around. Already there have been
a few miscarriages. People are scared to death."

Uncle Ohan said: "He may be a little off, being Great Meherr's
son. But herding cattle is good training for a fighter. Once he
learns the difference between a bear and a bull he will be all
right. He is all we have if we expect to make a stand against
the heathen."

"When is he going to learn?"

"He is an utter, complete fool."

Curses and anathemas.

While David slept in the town square the bears and boars
and tigers and lions escaped to the mountains, and in the morning people opened their doors and took their cattle in. He said:
"They are crazy. They let the fat sleek ones go and keep the
skinny ones."

David understood how people felt about him and said to
Uncle Ohan: "If they don't want me as a drover, let somebody
else herd their cattle. I will not. And, I don't care to live here
any more. I am going away."

Ohan lost his temper: "If that's the way you feel about it,
I cannot keep you in my home any more. You can go where
you like."

Uncle Toros came to Sassoun the next day and said: "Where
is David?" Nobody seemed to know. He searched for him and

found him sleeping in his hideout. He kicked him so hard that if it were not David but somebody else he would have driven him seven cubits under the ground. David woke from his sleep and said: "Uncle Toros, why are you kicking me?"

"Boy, what have you done?"

"I had so much trouble herding their cattle."

"You brainless Sssoun fool, mixing all the wild beasts with our herds. We don't want the ones that are always running away. Let them go."

"Uncle Toros, I don't want to be a drover, and I don't want to stay in Sassoun any more. I want to go to another country."

Uncle Toros took him to his own home, and David got his job back, and returned to Uncle Ohan's after staying idle for some time. He was ordered to take the herd to White Rock and to work with the drover of another village. Uncle Ohan gave him a new pair of steel boots and a new steel crook. "If I have to buy you new boots every day nothing will be left of your wages," he said.

David found another herd grazing at White Rock and added it to his own. A man ran after him, cursing him loudly. David turned around and raised his crook. "Were you cursing me? If I struck you once you would go down to the bottomless pit. Where are you from?"

"I am from Kel."

"What's your name?"

"Kyrakos. Where are you from, and what's your name?"

"I am from Sassoun, and my name is David."

"I didn't know you were David."

"We are both herders, let us be brothers," David said.

They played ball together.

David said: "It is good to have somebody to play with and to talk to while herding cattle. I am new at this. Keep an eye on my herd while I take a nap."

"David, my soul, I will watch your herd every day. Let me build a shelter for you and you lie down and take your nap."

David stretched out under the shelter the other drover built for him and slept until sundown.

"Get up, David. Time to go home."

David said: "Kyrakos, from now on you take care of my herd, and I take care of you."

David drove his herd back without any wild animals mixed in it and without a single calf missing. Uncle Ohan met him and said in a joyous voice: "Son, everything is in good order."

During the early spring rains when the cattle were thin and some of them got stuck in the mud and shivered in the cold David pulled them out of the mud, tied their feet together, passed his crook between their legs, swung them to his shoulder and carried them back to their owners.

Women blessed him and said: "David, may God give you plenty and keep your sun ever bright. If it were not for you our cattle would have perished this year."

They fed him fried eggs, they gave him butter, cheese and eggs to take home, they threw an extra loaf of bread into his sack when he collected his pay. They treated him very well. The people of Sassoun praised him and said: "We have never had another drover as good as David."

In the summer the cattle filled out and became sleek and fat. Women churned butter, made cheese, curdled milk into madzoon, made chortan from whey.[9]

On the feast of St. Mary people go to church and cauldrons of porridge are cooked with minced meat,[10] which people eat in communal meals for the salvation of the souls of their dead.

David saw that the roads were full of peasants and princes on their way to the monasteries and churches, and everybody was on the go. His brother herder did not show up for some time and when he finally came with the herd of the other village David said: "Why are you late?"

"I went to church. I came without eating even a spoonful

of porridge. Today people will feast on roast lamb and porridge. They will play the lute, and dance, and sing and make merry from morning to night. We poor drovers have to work even on the feast of St. Mary."

David sniffed in the fragrant smoke that reached the pasture at White Rock. "What is that smoke I see over there?"

"They are cooking porridge."

"Could you bring me some of that porridge? I am starved."

"Man, how could I bring you enough porridge? You had better go and eat your porridge in our village. And bring me some."

"Watch my herd while I am gone."

David put his crook under his arm and went to the village where the porridge was being cooked. He entered a house and saw the porridge cooking slowly in three great copper cauldrons, each with four handles, set over the tonir.

He said: "Mamik, for the sake of your father's soul could you give me a little porridge for a couple of drovers? If anybody is poor, it is the village drover."

The old woman said: "Are you Lisping David?"

"Yes, Mamik."

"You mad fool of Sassoun, don't you know you cannot eat porridge on the feast of St. Mary until it is blessed by the priest? Wait until the church service is over."

"Mamik, I cannot wait. I am in a hurry. I have a herd to look after. Give me some of that porridge and I will go."

"Have you no fear of God? You cannot eat this porridge until the priest and the deacons come here and bless it."

She ordered him out of her house. He lifted one of the heavy coppers from the tonir, poured a bucket of melting butter on the porridge, passed his crook through two handles and raised the cauldron to his shoulder. Then he took a stack of flat sheets of freshly baked bread and put it under his arm, seized a couple of ladles, and saying, "These will do for spoons," strode out of the house.

The old woman ran screaming to church. "Lisping David came and took a copper of porridge and all the bread I baked!"

The churchyard was crowded. People sat around the tables talking. A few young men drank wine. One of these young fellows said: "Let's go catch him and give him a good beating. We can bring the porridge back."

An older man cautioned them about David. "For the love of God stay away from him. He is one of the Daredevils of Sassoun, belongs to Meherr's stock. He will kill you if you lay hands on him."

David hurried back to White Rock and put the copper down, to eat the porridge with his brother, but the other drover was in tears and beat his head with his fists. David said: "I forgot to bring the salt. Well, you can eat the salt later, when you get home. It's no use crying over it now."

"No, no, brother David, I am not crying for salt. While you were gone forty lawless mounted devs struck and took forty of our best calves. I was so scared I could not say anything. My tongue dried in my mouth."

David said: "That's nothing to worry about. Let us first eat our porridge while it is still warm, and then I will go after the devs."

"What am I to tell the owners of my stolen calves? They will take it out of my pay. I have lost my appetite. I can't eat, worrying about it."

David ate all the porridge himself. Then he got up and said: "Which way did the devs go?"

"I don't know — that way," said Kyrakos.

He took his crook and went after the forty robber demons. He ran uphill, downhill, looking for them. He saw a thin column of smoke rising from a hilltop and suspected it was the hideout of the demons. He went up the hill and called out in a loud voice: "Hey, you lawless devs, bring those calves back or I will wring your necks." When the demons heard him in their cave they shook with fear, like forty devils hearing Christ's yelling in hell. They said: "That is David, Meherr's son, coming after us. He belongs to Sanasar's stock and the mad fool will kill us surely if we do not become his servants and give him what he wants. He may spare our lives if we surrender."

David saw that the demons had already slaughtered the forty calves and were cooking them in a cauldron of forty handles. The stew was simmering on burning pine logs.

He crouched behind a rock and waited for them to come out of their cave. The cook came out first, to put salt in the stew. David struck him on the head with his iron crook and flattened him to the ground before he could utter a sound. Then another demon came out to see what happened to the cook. One blow from behind the rock, and the dev was dead. A third one ventured out, and David wrung his neck. They came out of the cave one by one, and David killed all forty of them. He waited to see if there were any others, but these were all. He got up and entered the cave. It was furnished with rugs and cushions and everything they needed for their comfort and kef.[11] He smashed an inner door open and saw the room was full of red-gold pieces. He smashed another door, and saw a roomful of silver coins. A third door led to the secret stable, where he counted forty horses, one of them a young colt. He could press down the backs of all the horses except the colt's. He kicked. His feet struck the ceiling of the cave and the rocks blazed with fire. "Bread and wine, the living God, all I want is this fiery colt," David said.

He filled his pouch with gold pieces, rolled a boulder that fifty men could not move and placed it against the entrance of the cave, cut off the ears of the dead demons and piled up their bodies before the cave, put a couple of ears in his pocket and hid the rest under a rock. He lifted the copper of forty handles and turned it over, put the hides of the slaughtered calves in it, passed his crook through a handle and raised the copper to his shoulder.

He strode back to the house of the old woman where the

porridge was cooked. The priest was just blessing the food.[12] He put the copper down with the hides of the forty slaughtered calves in it and said: "Mamik, here is a much larger cauldron for you than the one I took this morning. Forty robber devs stole forty of our calves and slaughtered them before I could get to them, but the hides of the forty calves are in this copper. Give them to the poor. I am paying for your stolen calves." He opened his pouch and placed a fistful of gold coins on the table.

The villagers said: "We thank you, David. We are satisfied."

"But let me warn you that if you take a handful of millet out of my brother drover's pay I will come back and level this house and this whole village to the ground, and it will be known as David's Ruin."

David ate some more porridge and hurried back to White Rock. His brother was still crying. David showed him the two ears in his pocket and said: "I killed the lawless devs. All forty of them. You take your herd and go back to your village. Don't worry about losing any wages. I have paid for the stolen calves. I warned their owners that if they take a handful of millet out of your pay I will level their homes to the ground and the village will be known as David's Ruin."

They separated their herds and David took his back to Sassoun, though it was early in the afternoon. The owners of the missing calves cursed him. He asked them: "How much is your calf worth?" If they said one silver coin, he gave them a gold coin. "I am through with herding cattle," he said, and went home.

Uncle Ohan was out. Sara saw David curl up in a corner of the room and take a nap. She said: "You lazy good-for-nothing. You didn't want to work as a goatherd, and now you don't want to work as a drover. Who will feed you?" She beat him with an iron skewer.

David was asleep when his uncle came home. Uncle Ohan woke him up.

"Is this the right time to bring the herd back from the pasture? Couldn't you wait a little longer?"

"Uncle Ohan, don't be angry with me. Let me have the colt, and you can have the rest."

"What colt, what are you talking about?"

"Uncle Ohan, we would need forty sacks to haul all that treasure away. But the colt is mine."

"May God blight your life, son, I don't know what you mean."

"Uncle Ohan, we are rich! I don't have to herd cattle any more, we can build a new house, we can live like kings with all that gold and silver."

"You must be out of your mind, boy, or did you just dream about it? You just bring home a few measures of millet and wheat and forget the silver and gold."

"Uncle Ohan, I killed the forty lawless devs. Their hideout is a treasure house, the warehouse of the world."

"You are lying, David."

He showed his uncle the ears he kept in his pocket. "You can cut off my ears if I am lying."

He shook the remaining gold coins out of his pouch. Ohan embraced the boy and cried: "David, my soul, you *did* kill the lawless devs! They are forty brothers who have been plundering our country ever since your father died." He kissed the boy on his red cheeks.

"The cave is full of gold and silver, and there are forty horses in the stable. Just give me the colt, Uncle Ohan."

They took forty sacks with them, mounted a couple of mules, and rode out to the cave of the robber demons. When Uncle Ohan saw the big pile of bloated bodies he jumped back on his mule and fled. They looked grisly in the moonlight.

David laughed. "I am not afraid of the live ones, are you afraid of the dead ones? Here are their ears." David took the ears from under the rock and showed them to his uncle. He rolled the boulder to one side and they entered the cave. Uncle

Ohan danced with joy as they filled their sacks with gold and silver. They loaded them on their mules and the thirty-nine horses of the demons. Ohan said: "They took it all from us. We will store all of this in the town treasury. Sassoun can use this gold and silver. We have taxes to pay." He helped David roll the bodies of the forty devs into a ravine.

For himself, David took only the colt, and rode him on their way back to town.

NOTES

[1] Jereed: a military game played with the javelin. An Arabic word.

[2] Polo, or an early variety of it. The Armenian word is *hol*.

[3] Liter: an Armenian weight, from Greek litra, that varies from place to place, and equals about 12 pounds.

[4] A mother's curse is dreaded in the Near East. An Arabic word, *haram*, is used here, which means unjust, unlawful, not right, bad, with its opposite being *halal*. Both words are used in Armenian colloquial speech.

[5] In a few variants there is a brief episode about the occupation of Sassoun by Misra Melik while David is in Egypt, and Ohan is held captive.

[6] Cutting off the ears of a corpse is still practiced in some Mohammedan countries as proof of death; or as a refinement in torture.

[7] Bulbul: a song bird, the Armenian nightingale. A Persian word.

[8] Steel boots: perhaps leather boots with steel nails, and not the usual sandal or moccasin still worn in country districts, but the word *sol* here suggests the solleret or flexible steel shoe of the medieval armor in western Europe.

[9] Madzoon is yoghurt. Chortan is dried whey, but may be made also from yoghurt.

[10] In country districts no holiday feast is complete without this porridge, *harisa*, cooked slowly in the *tonir*.

[11] Kef: making merry, feasting and drinking and enjoying oneself.

[12] The Armenian mass is so long that by the time the porridge is blest David could conceivably kill the robber demons.

CYCLE THREE: PART TWO

DAVID REBUILDS HIS FATHER'S MONASTERY AND PUNISHES THE TAX MEN

DAVID found a fine saddle and bridle for his colt and rode around all day, and sometimes he went to the priest's house, picked up the book, and read the Psalms. After killing the robber demons he was a popular figure in Sassoun and a valued member of Uncle Ohan's household. One day his uncle[1] called him and said: "David, we plow the field tomorrow. Plowing is pleasant work." David said: "May God preserve your home, Uncle. We have all that gold and silver in the treasury — and do we still have to work?"

"Son, we have taxes to pay. And it is not good to stay idle."

They rose early in the morning, and his uncle yoked a pair of oxen to the plow, and they went out to the field together. His uncle turned a few furrows and said: "This is the way we plow. Now let me see you do it yourself."

David took hold of the handles and pressed down on the plow. He could not make the oxen go. They sank to their knees. "Uncle Ohan, what is this? Why don't they move?"

"Boy, you are strong. They cannot move with you holding the plow."

"Uncle, come unyoke them. I want to see if I can plow this field without oxen."

The oxen were unyoked. David laid the yoke on his own neck, threw the chain around him, and dragged the plow without any difficulty. "Uncle, I don't need the oxen, I can plow without them." His uncle took the oxen and went home. David continued plowing. He plowed and plowed until he reached the millet field of the old widow, Barav. She was baking bread. She stepped out of her cottage and saw David plowing under her millet. She screamed from the door: "What are you doing in my field, Lisping David? Why do you plow under my growing crop? Have you no heart? I am a poor widow with one lame daughter and this millet field is all I have."

David said: "Mamik, plant it to wheat. For a change eat wheat bread for a while."

She struck him with her fists and drove him out of her field.

Uncle Ohan had to keep the boy busy and let him hunt with a falcon. The millet field was full of quail. Barav saw him in her field again, riding his colt with a falcon on his fist.

"David, may the angel of death strangle you, may you rot under the ground. You ruined my millet. Are you going to live on the meat of my little birds? Why don't you go to the mountains if you are such a brave hunter? You will find plenty of wild sheep in the mountains for your supply of preserved meat."

David said: "Barav, I have nothing to hunt with in the mountains. My falcon cannot kill wild sheep."

"Your father hunted with his great bow. Ask for it." She had been Meherr's sweetheart.

"Who has it? Where can I find it?"

"Ask your uncle or his wife. They know."

David went home and asked his uncle's wife: "Aunt Sara, where is my father's bow?"

She said: "May I die for you, David, I do not know. I have seen him with it, but I cannot tell you who has it now."

A little later David said: "Aunt Sara, I am hungry."

Sara said: "We have no bread in the house. Go to the woodshed and bring some firewood and I will bake some bread for you."

David rose and went to the woodshed, where he saw something hanging on the wall — a long curved stick covered with dust. He took it off the wall and carried it to the house with a load of firewood.

"Aunt Sara, what is this curved stick?"

She said: "I do not know. Ask your uncle."

David said, in an angry voice: "Aunt Sara, tell me, what is this curved stick?"

Sara said: "If you can attach this cord to it I will tell you."

David bent the stick and strung it. Sara was amazed. She said: "It took Meherr an hour to string it. That is the bow he hunted with."

David was glad to have his father's great bow. He washed it, cleaned and polished the metal parts, and he went hunting with it every day as his father had done.

A month or two later David was passing by the millet field again and saw a flock of crows descend upon it and eat up the grain. He wondered: "How can I kill twenty of these crows at once before the others fly off?" He ripped up a huge poplar tree by its roots and went after the crows and swept away the millet and the crows, making one big pile of both. Barav came out of her cottage and saw her field completely ruined; not a stalk of millet was left standing. She cried out: "Oy, oy, what have you done to my field? May God's fire strike you dead, but even lightning is too good for you. If you are angry about something why take it out on my field? How can you be the son of Lion-Meherr, may God bless his soul. He was a father and mother to poor people like us. But what have you done? This millet was all I had and you came and ruined it. My lame daughter and I have nothing left to live on."

David said: "I just wanted to save your millet from the

crows." He threw the tree away and gave her a fistful of gold coins.

The old widow said: "David, if you are so brave and if you like hunting so much why don't you go to your father's game preserve at Dzovasar? That's the place to hunt, my boy. Stocked full with every kind of wild game—wild bulls, and wild sheep and goats, and deer and stag, and wolves and bears and foxes and wild boars – you will find there everything you want."

David said: "Mamik, may I die for your soul, your sun, tell me how to go to Dzovasar. Where is it?"

"Your Uncle Ohan can show you the way. Ask him. Make him tell you."

David hurried home and said to his uncle: "Show me the way to Dzovasar, I want to go to my father's game preserve."

Uncle Ohan said: "Who told you about it?"

"Barav, who owns the millet field."

"May her tongue dry in her mouth. She lied. I know nothing about your father's game preserve."

"Uncle Ohan, you are not telling me the truth. If I were not afraid of God, I would slap you so hard I would break your neck."

Ohan saw the mad mood coming over David, and he was afraid of him. "Son, your father's game preserve is now Misra Melik's property. Nobody has been there for years. We keep out of it. We do not want to get in trouble with Melik."

"Dzovasar belongs to us. I want to see it."

"Son, it is too far away, and the nights are very cold there. You are too young to hunt in Dzovasar. If Melik hears about it he will be furious. You are too young, and I am too old to fight the heathen. We do not want another war with Egypt."

There was no arguing with David. Ohan talked it over with his brother Vergo and with Uncle Toros, and David said to his companions: "Boys, get ready to go to Dzovasar with me tomorrow morning." Preparations were made for a hunting trip and they started out early in the morning, with David heading the group as he rode his colt. The men who went along with him said: "We want to see David kill a few wild sheep." On their way to Dzovasar they came to a big poplar tree, and David reached up and pulled it down. He used the poplar tree as a swing. Uncle Ohan said: "Do you think I am not strong or brave enough to do it? Watch me." David relaxed his grip on the tree and up, up went Ohan, his feet dangling in the air. David swung him up and down a few times and let him enjoy himself.

They rode to Dzovasar and halted before a massive wall. David said: "What is this wall?" Ohan said: "This is your father's game preserve." David went up a mountain and looked around; he saw the wall going clear around the mountain. He came down and crying out, "Marouta's High Mother of God," kicked the one door open. They went in. And what did David see? A beautiful green park with all kinds of trees and shrubs, a fountain splashing in a pool, and the whole park full of bears and foxes and wild boars and hares and wild sheep. Unable to get out of the preserve they had multiplied in numbers and nobody had disturbed them for years. Everybody began hunting for himself. David called out to his companions: "Wait! I will not let anyone get too close to these beasts, it is wrong to kill them, they are prisoners and their meat is not good for eating. Even my doddering grandfather can shoot a wild sheep that cannot escape. If you are real men you hunt out in the open. My father sinned by building this game preserve."

He smashed the walls with his mace and let the wild beasts go. He threw up his cap and shouted, "Hoy-Hoy! Go, live free." He ran uphill and downhill and through rocky gorges to make sure all of them got out. He looked behind trees and rocks and said: "Maybe one of them is still sleeping somewhere . . . it would be a pity."

After he drove all the wild beasts out of his father's preserve he said to the men who came with him: "Now you can go after them if you like." Some of them hunted out in the open; the lazy ones stayed in the preserve. David caught a couple of wild sheep himself. He took off his clothes and plunged into the pool; then he stretched out on the grass and took a nap. After he bathed in it, he destroyed the pool too and ripped up trees by their roots. He said: "I will leave nothing to Melik." He made it David's Ruin.

They sacrificed the wild sheep to God, and built a blazing fire. They trimmed and carved the meat, cut it into small pieces, and David spitted them on his arrows. When the flames died down they made kebab, roasting the meat over the glowing embers. After their meal they sat around and talked, and then the other men got up and went home.

Uncle Ohan said: "David, it is time for us to go home, too. It is getting dark."

David said: "You go home if you like. I am staying here tonight."

"David, people do not sleep in these wild mountains. I would be afraid to."

"My father spent much of his time here hunting. I never got to know him, and here I feel close to him."

Uncle Ohan said: "If you stay, I stay. I cannot leave you here alone."

They pulled their hairy capes about their shoulders and lay down under a tree. David was soon asleep. Ohan tucked the skirt of David's tunic under him, for fear the boy would get up in the middle of the night and wander off by himself. The mountains here were full of wild beasts.

David awoke when Ohan himself was asleep. He sat upright and gazed around him. He saw a fire burning on the jagged peak of the mountain. Green-red flames shot up high into the sky and an arc of unearthly light spanned the starry heavens. "I would like to know who is on top of that mountain," he said to himself. He made an effort to get up, and saw that the skirt of his tunic was under Ohan's knee. Ohan was a big, heavy man. "My God," David said, "if I wake him up he will think I am afraid of the dark." Presently Ohan himself was awake, and

David asked him: "What is that green-red light flaring on the mountain?" Ohan knew the light came out of Meherr's tomb but he lied to David and said: "I do not know, son. Probably some drovers or goatherders, or perhaps travelers, are keeping themselves warm in this cold night."

"No, Uncle Ohan, I think this is another kind of light, not man-made."

Ohan turned over and went to sleep. David was not satisfied with his uncle's answer. The light burned in the form of a cross that moved up and down on the mountaintop. "If I cut off my skirt with my dagger I will ruin my tunic," David thought. "Well, why worry about it? To Gehenna with my tunic." He drew his dagger and cut his skirt, leaving the other end under Ohan's knee. He picked up his bow and quiver and moved noiselessly toward the green-red light. He climbed the mountain and saw a marble stone split wide open. The light came out of this stone. It was bright like day on the summit. His heart trembled as he approached the fire-light and held his hand against it. His hand did not burn. He threw a few handfuls of earth over the flames, and the fire continued burning. He said in his mind: "This must be Marouta's High Mother of God." He shot an arrow from his bow and left it sticking in the ground. He measured the tombstone: six feet wide and twelve feet long. He climbed down the mountain and went back to where his uncle lay. Ohan was still sound asleep. David stood over him and sang:

> "Awake dear uncle from your pleasant sleep
> I have no father, be father to me;
> I have no brother, be brother to me;
> I have no mother, be mother to me."

Ohan sat up and said: "Fool David, why don't you let me sleep, why are you so restless tonight?"

David sang as in a trance:

"Blessed is our merciful Lord
And infinite is God's love
And care for mortals below,
The marble tombstone I saw
Split open on the mountain
Sent up a wondrous light
That spanned the sky of Dzovasar
In an arc awesomely bright
And the cross over it gleamed.
I saw it all in my dream."

He let his uncle think it was only a dream. He did not say "I went there."

Ohan was now wide awake himself. He saw that part of the light fell on David. They went up to the monastery together and Ohan thought: "He will fight Misra Melik and free our people." David asked him: "Whose tomb is this?"

"Your father's. This is Marouta's High Mother of God, the monastery your father built. Misra Melik came and destroyed it, and we have not been able to rebuild it since then. We are afraid. We keep out of here, too. I did not want to tell you."

David approached his father's grave on his knees. He kissed the marble stone three times. Then rising to his feet he drew a line around the tomb with the tip of an arrow. He designed with his arrow a new monastery of forty altars to be built over his father's grave. He said: "I vow to rebuild this monastery, and this is the way we shall build it." He said:

"I expect from you by the hundred and thousand
stone cutters
I expect from you by the hundred and thousand
stone carvers
I expect from you by the hundred and thousand
gravel carriers
I expect from you by the hundred and thousand
water carriers

I expect from you by the hundred and thousand
    masons
I expect from you by the hundred and thousand
    plasterers
I expect from you by the hundred and thousand
    woodworkers.
May I drop dead if I ever break the oath I made
    tonight.
Have everything, men and materials, ready by to-
    morrow."

His uncle said: "Son, be a little patient and I will have everything ready for you. Don't worry, we will build the monastery. We have money in the treasury, and I am Ohan-the-Thunder-Voiced. I can be heard from seven cities, from places as far off as forty days' journey from here. Kill seven wild bulls for a great feast tomorrow. We can hire all the men we need at the feast."

David hunted down and killed seven wild bulls and they carried them to Sassoun with them. Uncle Ohan rose in the morning and called out at the top of his thunderous voice:

    "Hear me, hear me, Sassoun's firelight
    Is lit again, we shall rebuild
    Marouta's High Mother of God
    Take up your tools and come in haste
    To start today without delay.
        Oh I am calling, let them come
        He who loves God let him come.
    We need stone cutters, by the thousand
    Gravel carriers, water carriers
    By the hundred, by the thousand
        Oh I am calling, let them come
        He who loves God let him come.
    We need masons, plasterers
    By the hundred, by the thousand

We need wood carvers, masters and men
By the hundred, by the thousand
Oh I am calling, let them come
He who loves God let him come."

And the master craftsmen and the workers hired by the day poured into Sassoun and gathered for the feast at Ohan's house with all the Daredevils in town. They all went to Dzovasar and David himself did the excavating and trenching and carried huge stones on his back to the astonishment of the men working with him. He said: "'I bring them, you plaster them down." The other men carried small stones only. Even the girls and the young brides of Sassoun carried water and everybody, young or old, gave a helping hand.

The new monastery was built in seven days. Marouta's High Mother of God came to David in his dream and said: "David, draw your dagger and lay it under the foundation stone. Consecrate the new church at a great mass, and I shall rise upon that foundation."

David awoke from his dream and saw that the monastery was gone, disappeared from sight. The stones, the plaster, the gravel, the clay, the woodwork, everything had fallen apart and the building was just not there. He sprang to his feet and called out to his uncles:

"Awake, awake from your sweet sleep
Uncle Toros, Uncle Ohan
Marouta's High Mother of God
Said in my dream to build again
On my dagger and consecrate
The new church at a great mass."

His uncles were just as amazed by what happened during the night while they were asleep. Ohan said: "David, do not worry, I am Ohan-the-Thunder-Voiced and I shall call again in the morning."

He let out another mighty call, and master craftsmen and workers hired by the day came by the thousand-thousand with their tools. David drew his dagger and laid it under the foundation stone, and Marouta's High Mother of God rose upon it.

David said: "Uncle Ohan, be sure everyone is paid for his work." Ohan brought a few camel loads of gold and silver from the town treasury and standing before the monastery gate paid off the men one by one, each master craftsman receiving a gold coin, and each worker hired by the day a silver coin. These men returned happily to their homes.

David turned to Ohan-the-Thunder-Voiced and said:

> "I must have forty vardapets,
> Bring me forty archdeacons
> And also forty deacons
> And forty candle lighters
> To light the church on Saturday
> And celebrate holy mass
> With prayers, hymns, bread and wine
> To consecrate this sacred shrine."

Uncle Ohan rose up and called the clerics and they came in haste for the consecration of the new monastery, one of each rank for the forty altars. David put the cross on the tower and hung the bells. The forty altars blazed with wax candles and oil lamps, and there were priceless vestments embroidered in gold, and priceless crowns and miters, and priceless censers, and priceless crosses, and Bibles bound in gold and studded with priceless jewels David first saw in his dream. Marouta's High Mother of God was crowded with the devout of Sassoun and young and old took the holy communion during mass and all were glorified with David, praying with him for the salvation of his father's soul, Great Meherr.

David's heart was so gladdened by all this that he stayed in the monastery seven days. He brought Batman's Sword and the Demon of Frankistan and made them wardens of the gate, ordering that they be fed a goatskin of honey and a goatskin of butter every day. He said to his strongmen: "Open the gate to all pilgrims and the poor and the sick, feed them well and take good care of them, but keep out those bent on destruction." And he appointed Ohan of Aghbak guardian and superior of his monastery.

Misra Melik came to hunt in the game preserve with his pahlevans and found it ruined, with all the wild beasts gone. He went back to Egypt in a terrible rage and summoned his assembly. His councillors said: "May the King live long, send your constables to Sassoun to collect seven years' taxes. If the infidels pay their taxes, they didn't destroy your game preserve. If they refuse to pay them, then we know they did it and David is alive."

Misra Melik said: "I will take my horsemen and go to Sassoun."

A powerful pahlevan named Kouz-Badin, who was Ismil Khatoun's lover, rose in the assembly and said:

"May the King live long, it is not becoming that you go to Sassoun in person. Give me forty pahlevans and I will carry out your orders."

Misra Melik said:

"Sassoun must pay forty measures of silver and gold
Forty women tall in stature to load camels
Forty women short in stature to grind the grain
Forty women of middle size to play and sing
Forty virgins as personal gifts to me as King
Forty heifers, forty milch cows and oxen red."

Kouz-Badin said: "May the King live long, I will bring you also David's head. What will be my reward?"

"Your reward shall be a city, my brave commander. Now be on your way."

Kouz-Badin departed for Sassoun at the head of forty mounted pahlevans. As the squadron passed by a spring in the city where women were washing their laundry, spinning wool

and filling their jugs and gossiping, the women hailed the King's
men and sang and danced together:

> "Hey, Kouz-Badin of the wide grin
> Hey, you Soudin and Charkadin
> Where in such haste in battle-gear
> Why all this joy and all this din?"

Kouz-Badin answered them with a song:

> "We are going to sack Sassoun
> And haul away their girls and gold
> While infidels bury their dead
> We shall come back from our foray
> And bring you cows and oxen red
> And all summer you'll churn butter
> And make chortan for next winter."

A brazen young wench turned to Kouz-Badin and said: "Are you
going against those mad Daredevils? Watch out you do not fall
into the hands of that fair lad David."

Kouz-Badin said: "We will come back with David's head."
And touching his forehead with the tip of his sword he led his
horsemen, with bugles blowing and drums beating, to Sassoun.

Uncle Ohan was washing up in the morning when he saw the
Arabs pitching their tents in Lera-Plain and was afraid of what
David might do. He said to David: "Take your bow and spear
and go hunt in the mountains. Tonight let us have a wild sheep
for supper."

After David was out of the house Kouz-Badin came to Uncle
Ohan's and said:

> "You owe the King forty measures of silver and gold
> In unpaid taxes for seven years I must collect
> Forty women tall in stature to load camels
> Forty women short in stature to grind the grain
> Forty women of middle size to play and sing

Forty virgins as personal gifts to him as King
Forty heifers, forty milch cows and oxen red."

Uncle Ohan said: "Sit down and rest. Have a cup of tea or
coffee with me. I shall go to Misra Melik with you and either
pass under his beard or win his good will and respect so that
he will reduce our taxes."

They did not want to listen. They demanded everything to
be ready to be handed over to them in an hour. Seven of the
King's pahlevans fell on Ohan and tried to strangle him in his
house, until he agreed to give them what they wanted. Ohan
and Vergo went around with Kouz-Badin, Soudin, and Charkadin and collected forty tall women and locked them up in an
empty barn; forty short women and locked them up in a barn;
forty middle-sized women and locked them up in a barn; forty
lovely virgins and locked them up in a barn; also forty heifers,
forty red oxen, forty red cows the King demanded. Then they
led Kouz-Badin, Soudin and Charkadin to the treasury in the
fort.

David still hunted in the mountains and did not know what
was going on in the city. He came back with a wild sheep stuck
at the end of his spear. He stopped at the old widow's vegetable
patch, picked some turnips, peeled them with his rusty pocket-
knife and began to eat them. She was waiting for him with tears
in her eyes, her hands tucked in her blouse.

"The angel of death take you! May you rot under the ground,
you fool. You ruined my millet and now you are eating my
turnips when they have camped at our doorstep and taken away
my only daughter to be sold in slavery in Egypt. I cut the food
from my own mouth to bring her up as a decent Christian girl
and this is what happens, all because of you, you fool! You went
and destroyed Misra Melik's game preserve and now he is furious and has sent Kouz-Badin to collect seven years' taxes
from us."

"Mamik, what happened? I do not understand what you are

saying. Taxes? What taxes? Who is Kouz-Badin?"
She said:

"All Sassoun, my boy, is in that fiend's hold.
He wanted and got forty women tall
He wanted and got forty women short
And forty women neither tall nor short
And forty virgins for Melik himself.
To Melik belongs everything we own
We have to pay him seven years' taxes,
Oh David, my soul, do *we* pay taxes?
The women and girls are held in the barns
The heifers and cows and our oxen red
All are Melik's now. We are ruined, my lad,
This is the worst raid Sassoun ever had.
Forty camel loads of silver and gold
Are to be measured out — may God strike them dead.
The next thing you know he will want your head."

David seized her arm and said in an angry voice: "Mamik, where are my uncles?"

"You are pulling off my arm. Take your hand off me, and I will tell you. They are in the treasury room with Kouz-Badin, measuring out the gold and silver. Son, you stay away from that blood-thirsty monster. Go back to the mountains and save your head."

David said: "Mamik, do not worry about me."

David hurried to the fort. Instead of the usual happy talk and laughter at this time of day he found the town in a wild uproar. Such was the noise and confusion that parents denied their own children. Kouz-Badin's men were plundering the inhabitants, beating them up, taking hostages and burning down the houses of those who resisted. Women and children were screaming and sobbing aloud. David saluted the seven guards who stood at the entrance to the treasury with drawn swords. A crowd had gathered before the fort. They cursed David.

"May you rot under the ground! May you perish like a dog!" They all blamed him for the raid. He wanted to kill himself.

David said to the guards: "I am going in to help my uncles measure out the gold and silver we owe my brother, Misra Melik."

He strode into the treasury with the wild sheep on his shoulder and what did he see? Vergo was on his knees, holding a sack, and Ohan was measuring out the gold like so much barley or wheat, and both of them were soaked in sweat and looked exhausted. Kouz-Badin, Soudin and Charkadin sat around the room in comfortable chairs, and Kouz-Badin had one leg thrown over the other and was smoking his narghile.[2] He had enormous mustaches with sharp pointed ends, eyebrows as big as a man's hand, a cavernous mouth. When Ohan said, "This makes two measures," Kouz-Badin said, "One!"

Ohan saw David enter the room, but Vergo did not see him, and when David shouted at his uncles, "What are you doing here?" and Vergo looked up and saw David glaring at him he soiled his underwear. "David, death take you, this happened once before, I got colicky when your father yelled at me like that."

"Give that measure[3] to me," David said, putting down his wild sheep. "You go home and clean yourself. You are too old to do this." He helped Vergo get up to his feet.

"This is the last load of gold we have to measure," Vergo said.

"By God, I will measure this last load myself," David said.

Uncle Ohan said: "Son, don't get mixed up in this. You should not have come here."

David snatched the measure away from him and said: "I want to be sure my brother Melik gets every piece of gold we owe him. You hold the sack and I will measure it. This is the way to measure gold for Melik."

David turned the measure upside down, scooped up gold

pieces from the pile beside him, arranged them on the bottom of the measure, then he moved a stick across the bottom as though to make sure it was a full measure for the King — and swept the gold pieces back into the pile. He went through the motions of dumping the gold into the sack as he held the empty measure. "One — two — three measures!"

Kouz-Badin jumped to his feet. "Hey, Ohan, throw this crazy Armenian out. Did you bring this fool to make fun of Misra Melik? He is playing with us. If you want to pay your seven years' taxes, pay them. If you do not intend to pay them, let us not waste any time with this foolishness. I will go tell the King and he will come and level Sassoun to the ground." He turned to David: "Give that measure back to Ohan, or I will chop off your head." David stepped lightly toward the commander, leaned over and glowered at him with mocking blood-shot eyes. He asked him: "What did you say? I do not hear very well."

"You son of a bitch," said the commander, and slapped him. Then he brought his whip down on Ohan's head, who stared at David with tears in his eyes, but said nothing. David would not let him. What did David do? He lifted the measure and crying out, "Bread and wine, the living God, Marouta's High Mother of God," threw it at the commander, who bent his head down to one side, escaping certain death, and made a dash for the door. David grabbed him from behind, turned him around, slapped him a few times, breaking his neck and knocking out two of his teeth. Soudin and Charkadin were terror-stricken and tried to get out of the treasury room. David caught them and killed them on the spot by wringing their necks and wrenching their heads off as if they were a couple of chickens. He threw their bodies over the fortress wall and their heads into the yard.

David ran out and did the same to the guards at the gate, wringing their necks off like so many chickens. Kouz-Badin begged him: "Don't kill me, David, take pity on me." David said: "Fear not, Kouz-Badin, I will not kill you, yet. I want you

to go back to Egypt and give my regards to my brother Melik.
Tell him David pays no taxes and if he wants to collect them
he has to come for them himself. Forty virgins! My horse is
too good for his wife. I do not favor war and destruction, but
if he is King of Egypt I am master of Sassoun." David wrote a
letter and gave it to Kouz-Badin to deliver it to Misra Melik.
The commander mounted his horse and fled to Egypt. He was
scared to death.

David broke down the doors of the barns, freeing the women
and girls. "Sisters, mothers! You can go home now, you have
nothing to fear. Go home and pray for me." Barav tearfully
embraced her lame daughter, crying, "Glory be to God!" David
freed also the heifers, the cows and the oxen the pahlevans had
collected and said: "Go back to your owners, you creatures of
God." He went back to plowing Barav's field.

The hearts of Uncle Ohan and Uncle Toros and of all the
people in Sassoun shook with a dreadful fear. What would
Misra Melik do now? Kouz-Badin reached Egypt in shameful
disgrace. The King foamed in the mouth when he read David's
letter; many offensive things were written in it. So David was
alive and restored the House of Sassoun to its former power
and glory, and it was in truth David who destroyed the game
preserve, and rebuilt Marouta's High Mother of God after it was
wrecked by the King's orders.

Kouz-Badin said: "May the King live long, give me your
six-footed horse and five hundred men and I will go back to
Sassoun and settle our accounts with David. I will come back
with forty years' taxes this time, and David's head."

Misra Melik said: "Your reward shall be half of my kingdom."

Kouz-Badin took five hundred[1] mounted strongmen with
him as he rode back to Sassoun on the King's horse to take revenge on David, but when he came to Lera-Plain he changed
his mind about entering Sassoun. He said: "That fool David is
too strong and the infidels are afraid of him. He is their king

now. I will go strike at his monastery, where I hear there is enough gold and silver to gladden Melik's heart."

Kouz-Badin altered his plans and secretly led his army around Sassoun to Marouta's High Mother of God. Batman's Sword and the Demon of Frankistan saw the approaching horsemen and said: "These men do not look like pilgrims, they are all mounted; if they were pilgrims some of them would be traveling on foot. We will close the gate."

David's two strongmen acting as wardens of the gate fought like lions and killed two hundred of the marauders. Kouz-Badin shouted: "Open the gate! We are the King's men!"

They roared back: "We take orders only from David!" They fought them off for seven days and seven nights.

Kouz-Badin shouted again: "We have just come from Sassoun, where we killed David. Your master is dead and you have no one besides the King to protect you now. The King will forgive you if you re-enter his service. Here is David's bloody shirt, if you do not believe it."

A shirt like David's soaked in the blood of a fox was raised on a spear and thrown over the monastery wall. Then a couple of ears like David's were thrown over. Kouz-Badin continued his loud talk: "You can keep this gate closed until pitch turns white, but this monastery, like all of Sassoun, belongs to Misra Melik, and your situation is hopeless. No harm will come to you if you let us in. We want to rest here tonight."

The wardens of the gate and all the monks grieved over David's death. They said: "We are lost without David." Some of them scattered ashes over their heads. Kouz-Badin threatened, made promises. The superior of the monastery, Ohan of Aghbak, fearing the King's ire, and believing the false promises made by his commander, ordered that the gate be opened. Batman's Sword and the Demon of Frankistan fled to the mountains. Kouz-Badin stood in the doorway of the monastery and let his men in one by one. They massacred all the monks, stripped the monastery bare and took everything they could lay their hands on: the gemmed gold crosses and chalices, the gold-headed croziers of the vardapets, the gold censers and candle-sticks, the Bibles bound in gold, the brocaded vestments and altar curtains, the crowns and miters. Only a deacon working as steward who was out to fetch water from the spring was left alive, and Ohan of Aghbak, the superior, whom Kouz-Badin took with him.

This lone surviving deacon hid himself under the corpses thrown around the altars and when the Arabs were gone, leaving the monastery a bloody shambles, he picked up the surplice worn by a candle-lighter, soaked it in a pool of blood, and ran to Sassoun with it. David was feasting and drinking with his companions. He liked his wine and brandy, he had filled out, and his neck had grown so thick and red that you could not cut it with a saw. Uncle Ohan stopped the deacon at the door. "Why did you come? What do you want?" He did not want David to be disturbed during his kef. "The fool," the deacon said, and received a resounding slap from Ohan.

David called out from his room: "Who is it, Uncle Ohan, whom are you beating up now?"

"A deacon from the monastery, the steward, who called you a fool."

"The steward? Give him what he wants, oil, candles, incense, and let him go."

The deacon would not leave and insisted on seeing David.

"Let him come in," said David. He was blind drunk, and reclined on a rug, with one leg resting over the other, a wine cup in his hand. "Steward, are you short of supplies? Incense, oil, candles, is that what you want?"

"Who cares for them now?" the deacon said. "You can throw your oil and candles into the fire. You are sitting here making kef and do not know what happened to your monastery." He sang:

> "Alas a thousand times alas
> They slaughtered all the vardapets

Who held croziers of splendid gold
Preaching sermons at holy mass.
Alas a thousand times alas
They slaughtered all your forty priests
Who held the chalice made of gold
In giving holiness at mass.
Alas a thousand times alas
They killed forty deacons less one
Who swung thuribles made of pure gold
Toward the people blessed at mass."

David said: "I cannot make you out, deacon. Make it short, don't
give me a headache. You want incense, oil, candles? Take them
and go."

The deacon said:

"You are having here all this revelry
Eating goose and pilav and making merry
Drinking seven-year-old pomegranate wine
As if nothing were wrong, everything fine
When the lights in your church no longer shine.
They struck at Marouta's monastery
And slaughtered them all—forty vardapets
Forty archdeacons and forty deacons
Less one, myself, whom they did not see
Hide among the slain, only I escaped.
They took everything and left only this
And you eat and drink as if nothing's amiss."

The deacon unwrapped the bloody surplice and threw it to the
floor before David. David put down his wine cup and sprang
to his feet. "What is this, steward? What happened? Tell me!"

The deacon said:

"David our master, may your wine be sweet
But this is no time for such merriment
Forty vardapets lie slain on altars

Forty archdeacons and forty deacons
Less my sinful self lie slain in their rooms
They struck Marouta's High Mother of God
They smashed everything, they killed and they robbed."

"Who were they? Who?" David asked the deacon.
"Kouz-Badin, with five hundred horsemen."
"Who let them in?"
"Our superior, Ohan of Aghbak."
"Deacon, sit down and eat."

The deacon sat down and began eating. David picked up the bloody surplice and wept loudly over it. He was sober now. He sang this lament:

"God have mercy have mercy on King Gagik
God have mercy have mercy on Dzovinar
God have mercy have mercy on Sanasar
God have mercy have mercy on Balthasar
God have mercy have mercy on Great Meherr
God have mercy have mercy on Armaghan.
God have mercy have mercy on vardapets
Who hold the crozier when they preach the Gospel
God have mercy have mercy on the priests
Who hold the chalice when they give the law⁵
God have mercy have mercy on the deacons
Who swing the censer toward the people
God have mercy have mercy on them all."

David turned to the deacon and said: "When did they leave the monastery? Which way did they go?"

"They left shortly before I did and went south toward Egypt."

David turned to Uncle Ohan: "Uncle, didn't my father leave a horse, weapons, something? Bring them out and give them to me. I need them."

"No, son, your father left nothing. I have nothing of his to give you."

David turned to his companions: "Boys, girls, there is plenty to eat and drink in this house. The feast is not over. But Bread and wine, the living God, Marouta's High Mother of God, I am going!"

He rolled up his sleeves and without putting on his boots ran barefoot to the cottage of the old widow. "Mamik, which way should I go to overtake Kouz-Badin? He struck at my monastery last night and is on his way back to Misra Melik with his spoils. A deacon just brought me the news."

"Go this way, son, and wait for that fiend behind the big rock in the narrow Twin-Ravines near the Batman river. He has to pass through it and cross the bridge to get back to Egypt."

David ripped up a huge poplar tree by its roots, ran his hands down the branches and the trunk and converted it to a spear, and putting it on his shoulder ran toward the river. His uncle ripped up another tree, and followed him. Together they waited behind the big rock in Twin-Ravines, and were on the alert for the sound of horses' hooves or human voices. They could hear nothing but the clamor of the torrential river as it rushed down to the Tigris and they thought Kouz-Badin and his men had already crossed the bridge. They kept looking around and presently they saw them in the meadow farther up the river. They had turned their horses loose and their weapons lay on the ground beside them as they rested on the river bank. Some of them were sleeping in the shade, others were cleaning their clothes and boots or grooming their horses.⁶ David and his uncle heard Kouz-Badin boasting about his attack on the monastery and cursing David and his father. "Let David come after us if he can. Next time I will chop off his head for sure."

David called out to him: "Kouz-Badin, how are you going to escape from me this time?" Kouz-Badin looked around and saw David swoop down over his men toting a huge tree. David and his uncle swung their trees left and right and flattened out from ten to twenty men with each sweeping stroke of their poplars, and they swept the rest, with the bodies of the dead, into the river. Its thunderous waters seethed with Arabs gasping out their lives as David and his uncle continued to hit them on their heads and send them to the bottom of the Batman.

David caught Ohan of Aghbak alive and tore him in two from limb to limb. Kouz-Badin tried to get away on his six-footed horse but David caught him also. He knocked out his remaining teeth and strung them on his forehead like beads. He cut off his ears. He cut up his lips. He tore out an eyeball. He broke the commander's spear and had the pieces hanging from his neck. He broke his knees and arms, put him on his horse, and tied his feet under it.

"I should kill you, too, but go tell your King what David did to you and your pahlevans. I hope Melik does not try it again. Your horse knows the way back to Egypt."

David recovered the priceless church vessels and costly vestments and returned to Sassoun with his uncle. They buried the slain monks, cleaned and repaired the monastery, brought in forty new vardapets, forty archdeacons, forty deacons, and had Batman's Sword and the Demon of Frankistan guard the gate again.

It was getting dark when Kouz-Badin reached the spring where women gathered for their wash and filled their jugs and spun wool and gossiped. They saw him coming back, alone, and he tried to avoid them and enter the city by another route. Their husbands and brothers were not with the commander, and they mocked and reviled him with a song.

> "Hey, you braggart, foul Kouz-Badin
> Back from your raid to sack Sassoun?
> To haul away their girls and gold
> Forty women to load camels
> Forty women to grind the grain
> Forty women to play and sing
> Forty virgins, gifts to the King
> Forty heifers, forty milch cows

To make butter, to make chortan
Forty oxen, forty measures
Of white silver and yellow gold —
We look for all of this in vain.
What we do see are your big teeth
Strung on your head, your broken spear
Around your neck like a dog chain
Your gaping mouth buzzing with flies
Your swollen lips — you are a wreck!
You went howling like a wild wolf
And you come back like a whipped cur.
Where are our men? You left them there
You mean coward, to save your skin
We spit on you, vile Kouz-Badin."

Kouz-Badin sang back these words:

"Listen, women, don't talk and mock
Until you know the gruesome fact.
I thought Sassoun was a flat plain
It's up in clouds and it's all rock
A grisly place in sun or rain.
It's the abode of fierce madmen
Who shoot long logs from their great bows
When scarcely out of swaddling clothes
And so awesome is Sassoun's might
That on those heights the grass blades bite.
Swords of Sassoun strike like lightning
Your men had no chance in fighting
Those pahlevans, and floods next spring
Will I am sure their bodies[7] bring.
You can churn them into butter
And make chortan for next winter
If you call me a cowardly cur."

The women wept aloud and screamed curses on Kouz-Badin's
head as they went home without their men. Misra Melik in-

quired in the assembly: "Where is Kouz-Badin? I gave him my six-footed horse and sent him to Sassoun to collect seven years' taxes. He should be back by now. I have not seen him."

They searched for Kouz-Badin and found him hiding in the city. They dragged him before the King and a throng of screaming women gathered outside the hall of justice and demanded that he be punished. He was such a sorry sight that the King himself mocked him with a song in his savage anger.

"You were a fearless man in my divan
My boldest warrior, greatest pahlevan
Tell me, Kouz-Badin, what the infidels did
Where are my forty lovely virgin maids
Forty women tall for loading camels
Forty short women for grinding the grain
Forty camel loads of silver and gold
The infidels owe me. I thought by Allah
You would bring it all. Did you raid Sassoun
As you said you would wishing me long life?
Is not David dead? O where is his head?
I do not believe you even saw him
Do not lie to me, just tell me the truth
Say you fled from him, went into hiding
And lost the strongmen who rode out with you."

"May the King live long, how can you say I did not even see David?" wailed Kouz-Badin. "I attacked the monastery and killed all the monks but I was waylaid by David at the Batman river. I saw him coming after me with a great big poplar tree. He held the tree by the end and struck at us with the roots, left, right, like this, as though holding a sword, and he killed all my men or swept them into the river. I lost all the gold and silver I was bringing to you, O King! David has become a very bold reckless fellow, and if it were not for him our raid would have been a complete success."

Misra Melik was consumed with envy and hatred for David.

He rose and went home with his vizier. He said to his mother: "I was going to kill David, but you did not let me. I told you he would be the cause of all my troubles as King of Egypt. I told you you took a snake to your bosom, but you wanted to protect your orphan. Now he is in open rebellion against me, he kills my soldiers, he pays no tribute and taxes, he acts high and mighty and gives himself big airs as lord of Sassoun. He insults me, ridicules me and challenges me to go and collect the tribute and taxes myself, and by Allah I will go!"

Ismil Khatoun said: "My dear son, you did not do what I told you, you did what Kouz-Badin told you. I told you to visit David once or twice a year and invite him occasionally to our home, to act like his big brother. That would have made him happy and he would have said proudly, I have a brother. But what did you do? You sent Kouz-Badin against him. I cannot blame David for what he did."

"Look here, mother. I am an Arab, and David is an Armenian. How can an Armenian be my brother?"

Ismil Khatoun said: "Perhaps you are too young to understand, my dear, but Arabs and Armenians can be brothers. Many are. They visit one another, they are welcome in each other's homes, they trust and help and respect each other. David is no stranger to us. I nursed him at my breast and kept him like my own son, and he is your half-brother. Remember, you had the same father. If you had treated him well David would have done anything for you. I will answer his letter and try to reconcile you two."

"Mother, I forbid you to write to him, and do not try to reconcile us, that is impossible now. I always did what you told me and got hurt. Now either I kill David, or he kills me. There is no room for both of us in this world."

Ismil Khatoun said: "Melik, you cannot kill David."

He angrily walked out with the vizier. He was unwilling to take his mother's advice, but the vizier cautioned him against any rash action against David. The question of war or peace with Sassoun was put to the assembly, and all the great men of Egypt came to express their opinions. Many of them did not want war with Sassoun. They said David meant no harm and was quietly sitting in his home when Kouz-Badin struck, killing and plundering in the name of the King, and some even deplored particularly the raid on the monastery. Men with a sense of justice were not lacking among the Egyptians.

But there were also others who said privately to the King: "David today is twenty years old. He is still too young and inexperienced to wage war against a great empire like Egypt. If you do not fight him now, he will come down to Egypt and kill you when he is thirty, that's sure. It is this year or never. Strike before it is too late."

Misra Melik rose in the assembly and declared to all the princes and pahlevans of Egypt from his throne:

"I will wipe out these infidels and I will build a new city on the ruins of Sassoun, so that the name of this accursed city will never again be mentioned in my presence, or remembered in the world. The infidels of Sassoun must be destroyed to the last man, and their women, children and possessions divided among the faithful."

The King stabbed his forehead with his razor, filled a vat with his blood, dipped his quill in the vat, and wrote out this order:

"Dispatch this letter I write with my blood
To the Shah of Iran
Dispatch this letter I write with my blood
To the Turkman Khan
Dispatch this letter I write with my blood
To Sultan Mourad
Dispatch this letter I write with my blood
To the King of Russ[8]
Dispatch this letter I write with my blood
To the King of Franks

Dispatch this letter I write with my blood
 To the English King
Dispatch this letter I write with my blood
 To the east and west
To seven kingdoms whose aid I request
Crusading barons[9] with axlike teeth and with
        hawklike heads
To my beglerbegs,[10] to all my subjects who can carry
          arms
This is war, men, this is war, merciless war against
         Sassoun.
I need forty thousand beardless young men
I need forty thousand just-married men
I need forty thousand dark-bearded men
I need forty thousand gray-bearded men
I need forty thousand red-bearded men
I need a hundred thousand white horsemen
     Ah, my white horsemen!
I need a hundred thousand red horsemen
     Ah, my red horsemen!
I need a hundred thousand black horsemen
     Ah, my black horsemen!
I need a hundred thousand pipe players
     Ah, my pipe players!
I need a hundred thousand drum beaters
     Ah, my drum beaters!
I need a hundred thousand foot soldiers
     Ah, my foot soldiers!
Come all, heed my call, this is war, men, war
This is merciless war against Sassoun."

Town-criers repeated the order in all the cities and hamlets of
the kingdom, and every male from twelve to sixty had to take
his arms and report for military duty. The troops poured into
the city and sharpened their swords and spears for the assault
on Sassoun.

NOTES

[1] DS, vol. II, p. 215. The name of David's uncle in this plowing episode is Zenjil Kheran, but the uncle referred to is still Uncle Ohan or Uncle Toros, which are often interchangeable. On p. 285, when David replaces a team of seven to eight pairs of buffaloes in the ploughland, it is Uncle Toros. David's plowing is mentioned several times in a few variants, with or without Ohan.

[2] Narghile: water-pipe.

[3] This measure, *kot,* is a round wooden container with a flat bottom and two handles.

[4] The number of strongmen Kouz-Badin takes with him varies.

[5] Law: holy communion.

[6] DS, vol. I, p. 626. The name of the uncle who helps David kill and sweep the marauders into the river is not given, but Uncle Ohan is at David's side with a tree of his own in other episodes.

[7] In the original variants we have "four-letter words" and a more correct translation would be "private parts."

[8] Misra Melik appeals also to the Kings of Russ, Franks, England, DS, vol. I, p. 908.

[9] Crusading barons: DS, vol. II, p. 294; vol. II, p. 382. Crusaders sometimes served in the Arab armies as mercenaries. Today baron means simply mister or sir.

[10] The beglerbegs (or beylerbeys) were governors of provinces in the Ottoman Empire; among Kurds beg is a hereditary title of a great landlord and tribal chief. Originally a Seljuk or Arab title of supreme commander or prince of princes.

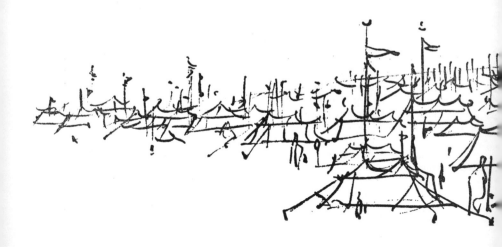

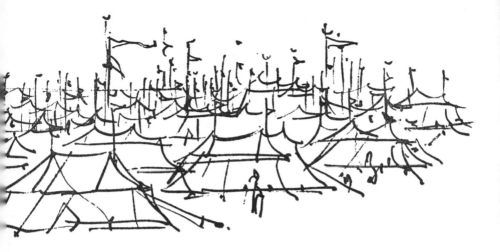

DAVID FIGHTS MISRA MELIK IN SINGLE COMBAT

THREE-FOURTHS OF the world was in Misra Melik's hands, and he was happy to see countless horsemen coming to his aid from the four corners of the earth. He sang out in joy as the mounted troops poured into his city:

> "Here they come, they come, all these beardless boys
> They come by hundreds, by thousands they come
> Here they come, they come, with beards just-growing
> They come by hundreds, by thousands they come
> Here they come, they come, my clean-shaven men
> They come by hundreds, by thousands they come
> Here they come, they come, my men with thick beards
> They come by hundreds, by thousands they come
> Here they come, they come, with drums and bagpipes
> The seven armies of my seven kings
> This is war, Melik, war against Sassoun."

They struck their tents in the plains of Egypt and asked Misra Melik: "Who is our enemy, whom shall we fight?"

He said: "David of Sassoun."

That night his mother, Ismil Khatoun, lost her sleep and ran to his bedside. She said:

> "Do not fight David, I warn you once more
> I saw three bad dreams and dread what they mean.
> The star of Sassoun was boldly aglow
> While Egypt's star dimmed. Then I dreamt again
> The horse of Sassoun attacked Egypt's horse
> And put him to flight. Worst was my third dream
> It was a sunny warm day in Sassoun
> But cold in Egypt, with hail, rain and mud
> The flood waters rose in the ghastly storm
> With corpses afloat, turning to dark blood.
> Son, take my advice and call off this war."

Melik said: "Hush, mother, speak no more. You lied and deceived me, and I shall no longer follow your advice. Why is your heart grieving for David? My armies are ready to strike, and I will wipe out the infidels of Sassoun. No, mother, I cannot call off this war. That is impossible now."

"Then I am going with you," she said.

"You are a woman, you stay here."

"I cannot stay here without you, waiting for you to come back."

Ismil Khatoun gathered forty unmarried girls and forty young brides, and fiddle-players and pipe-players, to sing and dance during the fighting, and left for Sassoun with her son. The King's wife and sister and his son Khosrov went along.

Misra Melik led his armies, riding his six-footed fiery warhorse, surrounded by seven kings and the seven pashas of Egypt. They rode day and night and reached the Batman river on the border. Those in the front ranks drank up half of the river, those coming from behind drank up the other half, and no water was left for those in the rear; they licked the sand with their parched tongues to slake their thirst.

Misra Melik camped in Lera-plain and wrote a letter to
Uncle Ohan and David: "I have come to collect the tribute and
taxes you owe me, and challenge David to fight me. I will turn
my armies loose upon Sassoun, kill all the males, seize the women,
burn down the city, and carry everything before me as in a
flood if you persist in your rebellion. You have ten days to give
me your answer."

The King's messengers delivered the letter to Uncle Ohan.
He read it and said: "My God, we have no arms and no army,
how can we fight against Melik? All we have is a mad lisping
boy." Tears trickled down his beard. "May God have mercy
on us."

Misra Melik's arrival struck terror in the hearts of the Sassounians, but David as yet knew nothing about it. They did not
tell him. Since Kouz-Badin's raid on the monastery and the
massacre of the monks, David was no longer himself and did
not know whether he was coming or going. He did not recover
from the blow, and remained gloomy and disconsolate.

Uncle Ohan took the King's letter to Vergo. When Vergo
also read it and learned of the innumerable tents pitched in
Lera-plain he said: "Ohan, there is nothing we can do, we cannot fight them, we have to collect the women and girls, the gold
and silver, everything Melik wants, hand them over to him, and
pass under his sword. Maybe he will take pity on us and spare
our lives. David must not know about it. We have to get him
drunk and keep him home until it's all over."

Uncle Ohan called a secret war council and the princes and
chief men agreed to pay the tribute and taxes Melik demanded,
give him hostages, and save the city from destruction. David
saw groups of men talking among themselves in low voices; they
scattered at his approach, or fell silent, and he did not overhear
what they said.

Uncle Ohan gave a feast for David, and Uncle Toros, coming
to the feast, said: "David, if you are Meherr's son you can prove

it to me by drinking a copperful of wine. If you can't, you are nothing but a bastard."

David said: "Fill it up."

Uncle Toros filled it to the very brim, and David lifted the great copper bowl to his mouth and drank it up. He flung the empty copper to the floor, smashing the vessel. When they picked it up there was a hole in it. David got so drunk at the banquet that he lay down and fell asleep.

While David was still sleeping, Uncle Toros went through the town beating his drum and calling his kinsmen to arms. He called each man by his name.

> "Arise, arise, men of Sassoun
> It is better we fight today
> Better strike now and let us see
> Whom God will give the victory."

Uncle Ohan closed the four gates of the city and put watchmen on the towers. Uncle Toros took his mounted warriors and rode out to the lofty peak overlooking Lera-plain.

The next morning David was again in the millet field of the old widow, hunting with his companions, suspecting nothing. Barav had just baked her bread and stepped out to take a look at her millet. She chased after him and struck him with her fists.

"May the angel of death strangle you, you fool, you mad turnip-eater of Sassoun. I have been looking for you. It was an evil day you were born. You slaughtered Melik's men and now he has come and surrounded Sassoun with his armies, and he is going to kill all of our men and carry off the women into slavery and burn the city to the ground and destroy us all from our roots up if we do not surrender and let him take everything we own."

"Mamik, where is Melik?"

"Son, he has camped in Lera-plain, and you may count the stars in heaven but you cannot count their tents. He is waiting for Ohan's answer to his letter before he strikes. The letter was addressed to you, too."

"Mamik, if Melik has come to fight me, I am ready. God will give the victory either to him or to me. Don't cry, it is nothing to worry about, I am still alive, thank heaven, and able to give him a good reception."

Barav laughed. "With your rusty pocket knife, or your bow-and-quiver?"

"That's all I have. Or do you want me to fight with the wooden stick for poking the fire in your tonir?"

"No, fight him with my churn," she mocked.

This made him angry. "Bread and wine, the living God, Marouta's High Mother of God," he said and ripped up a poplar tree growing by the roadside, swung it to his shoulder, and began running. Barav screamed after him: "David, David, are you going to fight Melik's armies with a tree? Come back, you fool! Fighting your brother is not killing birds. And he is not Kouz-Badin. He is King of Egypt and the Lord of Baghdad and the Emir of India."

David came back. "What shall I do then? I have no sword, no spear, no war-horse, no army, nothing to fight with."

She said:

> "Didn't your father have a Lightning-Sword
> And Colt Jalali, a fiery war-horse?
> Didn't your father wear a mailed corselet
> And a golden belt, a golden helmet
> When he went to fight Egypt's lawless horde?
> Weren't there topboots of steel on his feet?
> What happened to the velvet cloak he wore
> His silver saddle with stirrups of gold
> His lute and trumpet, and the drum he beat
> When he spurred his horse and rode off to war?
> Isn't there a Victory Cross, you dolt
> That Meherr wore on his stout right arm?

The eucharistic cross will be your charm
Ward off all evil and keep you from harm
Now tell me, son, can you ask for more?"

David threw away his poplar and said: "Barav, where are they, where are all these things, where can I find them, tell me!"

"Uncle Ohan will curse me if I tell you. He has been hiding them. He will give you evasive answers when you ask for them. You would have to use a little force on Ohan, or get him drunk to loosen his tongue."

David slipped a gold piece into Barav's hand for damaging her millet and ran to Uncle Ohan. On his way he seemed to hear his father's voice speaking to him from his grave:

"David, my dear son, take my fiery horse
And my Lightning-Sword and my mailed corselet
Have my mighty mace hanging by your side
Set on your fair head my golden helmet
Take my silver saddle and the boots I wore
Have the Victory Cross on your right arm
And carry on you the wonder-working
Most holy emblem of our monastery
Before you stand up against Egypt's might."

David gave a feast for Uncle Ohan and got him drunk to loosen his tongue. He said at the feast:

"I have no father, be father to me
I have no mother, be mother to me
I have no brother, be brother to me
Where is Jalali, my father's war-horse?
And his Lightning-Sword, the mighty mace he cast
When he fought the heathen, his golden helmet
And his golden belt, his cloak of velvet
And his trousers wide, his topboots of steel
His silver saddle with stirrups of gold
His drum and his pipe, his lute and trumpet.

I want everything he left behind him
They are mine now and I must have them soon
If I am to fight and defend Sassoun."

Uncle Ohan would not blurt out his secret and said: "I don't
know what you are talking about, son. Somebody lied to you."

"No, it is not a lie."

David seized his uncle by his collar, raised him up and shook
him hard a few times, with Ohan's feet up in the air. "I could
kill you. Where are you hiding them? Misra Melik challenges
me and you tell me nothing about it. I cannot fight him naked,
with my bare hands. I want my father's arms and armor, and
I want his horse."

"Son, you are too young to fight Misra Melik."

"Do you take me for a child?"

"Melik is too powerful for us and your father left nothing for
you to fight with. Pay no heed to such lies."

It was useless. Uncle Ohan would not tell him. The next day
the old widow said to David: "Try Sara. You have to use a little
force on her too. She knows where they are."

"How can I force her to tell me?"

Barav told him what he should do. David went home with a
pocketful of sand and complained of a toothache. Sara put the
sand in the pan used for roasting wheat or chick-peas and lit a
fire under it. She said: "Put this hot sand in your mouth to
draw off the pain." He said: "Put it in my mouth yourself."
He seized her hand and pressed his own hand tightly over hers
while he held it down in the roaster. "Oh oh oh David, you are
burning my hand!"

"I will make you eat this hot sand if you do not tell me where
Uncle Ohan is hiding my father's arms and armor, and his horse."

"Do you want to kill me? Let go of my hand and I will tell
you."

He released Sara's hand. She said: "David, you will find
your father's things in our secret storeroom forty feet under the

ground. To go down to the storeroom you have to remove a black slab on the floor of the stable, and the Colt Jalali is kept there in a separate section you can enter through a small inside door."

Now that his secret was out, Uncle Ohan consented to give David the keys to the storeroom. David lifted the black stone and they went down forty steps to the underground chamber where Meherr's arms and armor were hanging on the walls. Ohan opened a chest inlaid with mother-of-pearl in which Meherr's splendid clothes were neatly folded and he took them out one by one and gave them to David.

"Where is my father's sword?" David said. "Here, son, in this large clay jar filled with pitch.[1] Pull it out if you can." David drew the great sword out of the pitch as easily as though he were pulling a hair out of dough. He looked at it: its jeweled hilt shimmered like a pigeon's neck. He kissed his father's sword three times and touched his forehead with it.

"Where is my father's mace?" he asked. The mace was used in the stable as a chicken roost. Forty men could not lift Meherr's mace and Ohan helped David carry it out of the stable and clean it.

David put on his father's clothes and armor. The helmet came down to his chin. They stuffed seven liters of cotton into it before he could set it on his head. The boots were so enormous he could not wear them without stuffing seven liters of cotton into them. The golden belt went three times around his waist. The sword was so huge and long that when he slung it from his shoulder half of it scraped against the ground and the other half stuck over his head.

David asked next: "Where is the Victory Cross?"

"That, son, I cannot give you. That is in God's hands. If you are a just man like your father and worthy of it you will se it on your right arm, embedded in your flesh like a battle-scar. You have to pray for the Victory Cross, cry for it, fight for it."

"And now let me have my father's horse," David said.

"You need your father's horse, son, if you are going to wear all these arms and armor. They are so heavy no other horse can carry them. David, after your father died I would not let his fiery horse out of the stable for fear Misra Melik would know about it and want him for himself. We have been feeding and watering him from the roof. I don't dare go near that horse. If you can lead him out of the stable, Jalali is yours."

David entered the secret stable through a little inside door no one had opened for twenty years. He had his father's armor on him and the horse smelled him with tears in his eyes, taking him for Meherr. David caressed his mane, stroked his neck and back, and the horse kept nuzzling him. David led him out of the stable. The horse kicked, with fiery sparks blazing out from his hooves, when he saw it wasn't Meherr. The horse spoke by God's order:

"Earthborn, what do you want to do with me?"

"I want to ride you to war," David said.

"Ride me? I will take you up to the clouds and burn you to ashes against the sun."

"I can ride under your belly."

"I will smash you to pieces against rocks and trees. I will hurl you against the winds. Throw you into bottomless seas. My name is Colt Jalali. If I just breathe on you you will be blown off like so much dust, you earthborn fool."

David said: "I can ride on your back, under your belly, on your right side, your left side. I can hang on to your tail. I can even ride in your mouth if I want to."

"Some rider," Jalali said. "From now on you are my master and I am your horse."

David kissed him on the head and said:

> "You had no master, I am your master
> No one to groom you, to hold your halter
> No one to feed you, to give you water
> To look after you, O Colt Jalali."

The horse was covered with a thick layer of dirt and looked pitifully thin and uncared for. David led him to Barav's and halted before the door of her cottage. She was happy to see Meherr's horse again. "That is your father's Colt Jalali," she said. David said: "Mamik, heat two copperfuls of water. I will go get a bar of soap from Uncle Ohan and let us wash and clean this horse before I ride him."

Uncle Ohan gave him the soap, but stayed away from the horse. He said: "He will kick and kill me if I get too close to him."

With David, the horse was gentle and quiet now. David said to Barav: "Hold his head, and let your daughter pour the water while I wash him." They soaped him and scrubbed him seven times. Then they groomed him carefully in the Arab manner. Ohan finally came over with a measure of barley and a load of hay and David fed his horse.

"Uncle Ohan, give me his silver saddle with the gold stirrups."

Ohan brought him the silver saddle with the gold stirrups and watched him saddle the horse, thinking to himself: "When Meherr mounted him Jalali reared up on his hind legs. If he will do that with David, I will let him go fight Misra Melik." All four feet of the horse were off the ground when David seized the silver saddle and put his feet in the gold stirrups. He rode up and down a few times and had Barav also enjoy a ride with him. Jalali had found his new master.

Uncle Ohan said: "Come, my boy, let us go to Marouta's High Mother of God with forty barren heifers and sacrifice them to God. Kneel and pray before the holy altar while mass is sung and maybe our merciful Lord will deem you worthy of being Meherr's son."

Early the next morning they drove the forty barren heifers to the monastery and sacrified them to God. David bathed in their fresh warm blood. He made his confession, took the communion, knelt before the altar seven times, said tearful prayers,

and received the holy emblem, the cross of Marouta's High
Mother of God, and a comb. He kissed the cross and kept it on
the right side of his breast, and he kept the comb on the left side.

Ohan said: "David, with this holy emblem on you you need
fear no evil." And he said to the superior of the monastery:
"We have only seven days left before Misra Melik lets his armies
loose upon Sassoun. Pray for David and have masses sung for
him for seven days and nights. I am letting him go fight Misra
Melik. When filled with God's grace, David may be the salvation of Sassoun and free us from the heathen."

Ohan kissed David on his cheeks. David returned to town
cured of his lisping.

David was ready. He looked small on the giant horse. Uncle
Ohan burst into tears and sang this lament:

> "There goes Sassoun's dreaded war-horse
> I hoped to give to the Frank Pope
> Alas, a thousand times alas.
> There goes Sassoun's silver saddle
> I planned to give to Iran's Shah
> Alas, a thousand times alas.
> There goes Sassoun's lightning-like Sword
> Helmet of gold and golden belt
> Alas, a thousand times alas."

David's hand gripped the hilt of his sword. Uncle Ohan added
in haste:

> "There goes Sassoun's handsome David
> Our proud young deer and fearless ram
> The bright firelight of Sassoun's House.
> Alas, a thousand times alas."

David said: "Uncle Ohan, I thought you were not going to mention my name. These last words saved your life."

"Son, what do you think I am crying for? I regret your
going most of all. You are all we have."

David jumped off his horse and kissed his hand. "Uncle Ohan, I thank you for all the love and care you have given me. May I be worthy of it."

People crowded in the streets as they heard the great war drum of Sassoun. The young brides of the city sang and danced before David.

> "Brother David, our gallant boy
> We hope and pray that you come back
> And fill our hearts with pride and joy.
> You are leaving before we could
> As a bride would welcome you home
> Help you dismount and hold your horse
> And pour water over your hands
> To bake your bread and make your bed."

David whirled around on his fiery horse and bowed courteously to the young brides and to all the people gathered around him. He played his father's lute and sang a cordial farewell:

> "Brothers, sisters, I thank you all
> It is God's will that I go fight
> Misra Melik with all my might.
> O my sisters, goodbye, goodbye
> Sweet sisters all you are to me
> For you I will most gladly die.
> O my mothers, goodbye, goodbye
> Sweet mothers all you are to me
> For you I will most gladly die.
> O my neighbors, goodbye, goodbye
> Sweet neighbors all, you are to me
> For you I will most gladly die.
> My life with you has been so brief
> As a neighbor I caused you grief
> Forget my faults, forgive my sins.
> O good women, when you bake bread
> For my portion mention my name.

And you good men who fill the cup
Remember me on our feast days
In sweet Sassoun. Sisters, mothers
Neighbors and friends, pray for my soul
I say farewell to all, to all."

"This sounds like Meherr's drum and lute," Golden-Braids said in her dark sunless chamber, when a servant brought her her food.

The servant said: "Your grandson David has put on his father's arms and armor, and is going to fight Misra Melik. He is playing Meherr's lute."

Meherr's mother came out of her mourning behind seven locked doors, deprived of all sunlight. She was a very old woman now and as she rose to her feet part of her dress fell to the floor in shreds. She opened a window and looked out. She saw David coming along at a trot and the horse stopped under her window. Golden-Braids called the horse by his name and said:

"O faithful horse, dear to Meherr
His son David, your new rider
Has no father, you father him
Has no mother, you mother him
Has no brother, you brother him
Take my grandson to Milk-Fountain
As you fly him to Lera-plain
Let him rest there, drink its water
As did Meherr, his blessed father,
And have him test his Lightning-Sword
Against Meherr's tall iron tree
Before going any farther.
I trust my boy to your good care."

The horse listened to her words with bowed head. She said to David: "Your blessed father taught him every trick and showed him all the roads. Let this fiery horse be your guide wherever you go."

David dismounted and ran up to her chamber. He had never seen her before. He kissed her hand and asked for her blessing. Golden-Braids kissed him on the head, blessed him, and cursed Misra Melik. She said: "Thank God, I have at last attained my heart's desire. Now I can die in peace."

David mounted again. Uncle Ohan came running after him. "Remember what your grandmother said about the Milk-Fountain and the iron tree. It is a most pleasant place to rest, a fountain of immortality in a flowery meadow, a wishing-well where your father always stopped on his way to war. You will be filled with God's grace at the Milk-Fountain and attain your wish. Unsaddle your horse, eat your bread there before you go any farther, and bathe in the spring. When you come to the iron tree and test your sword against it you have to cut it at one blow. Come back if you cannot, for that would be an ill omen. And remember to say your prayers when you are in trouble. Don't forget to call upon the Holy Mother of God in any difficulty. And stay on your horse, and follow his lead."

Ohan's wife said in a mocking voice: "David, if you think you are brave enough to take on Misra Melik, bring me one of his ears."[2]

Vergo said: "Ohan, let him go and learn his lesson. He thinks it would be like killing little birds in a millet field."

Ohan said: "David, it is not too late to accept Melik's terms. We have enough gold and silver in the treasury to pay our tribute and taxes. Melik has seven kings and seven armies with him. Well, we have a few fighters ourselves. I will have some of our men go with you."

David said: "No, Uncle Ohan, I do not need an army to fight Melik, and you stay out of this war. Have no fear, God is on our side. I have this sword and the Holy Emblem with me. My going is in my hands, my return in God's."

"Son, I will watch your star."

Uncle Ohan took David's trumpet and played a battle tune of the Sassoun champions on it. "Well, David, your fate — and ours — is now in God's hands. May God be with you. Strike hard at those lawless people. Uncle Toros will guard the main pass with his warriors, and my watchmen on the towers of the fort will warn us if Melik moves on Sassoun. Bread and wine, the living God, Marouta's High Mother of God!"

David saluted his uncles and all the people who came to see him off, and rode out of Sassoun at a fast trot. Once out of the city, he slackened the reins. He was headed for Dzovasar but could see nothing, so thick was the mist. The horse flew like a falcon through the fog. "I can trust this horse," he said. "Let him take me wherever he likes. I need not worry with such a horse under me."

Jalali covered a distance of seven days in one hour and stopped when he reached a spring on a high rocky peak. The fog cleared on the upper ridges of the towering range. The horse would not go any farther. David said: "I will break your neck. Don't be so stubborn. I thought you could take me across rivers of blood, and here you stop before this little stream." David dug in his spurs and said: "I will cut off your head." He drew his sword. The horse threw him off and spoke again by God's will:

"David, this is the spring of immortality, your father's Milk-Fountain. Did you forget what Golden-Braids and Uncle Ohan said about it? I can take you up to the sun and burn you to ashes, and I can smash you to pieces against these rocks. But I will spare you this time for your father's sake. You broke my ribs."

David was sorry. He got up and kissed Jalali on the head. He unsaddled the horse, took off his bridle, and let him drink his fill from the sacred spring. He cupped his hands and drank from it himself, and he splashed the cool sweet water against the broken ribs of the horse. While Jalali grazed in the grass,

David took off his clothes and bathed in the spring. Then he sat down, opened his saddle-bag and ate his bread. He put on his clothes and armor, drank some more water, it was so wonderfully refreshing, and stretched out in the meadow for a good nap. The horse shaded him from the sun by standing over him. David slept between his legs.

An angel came to him in his sleep and said: "David, David, wake up, your prayers have been heard, your wish has been granted, your sword will be invincible as long as the Victory Cross on your right arm does not turn black." The horse gave him a gentle kick to rouse him from his sleep. When he awoke, David saw the luminous gleam of the Victory Cross on his right arm. His clothes and armor were scattered in the meadow grass around him. He had to remove the seven liters of cotton from the golden helmet before he could set it back on his head, and even then it was too tight. And too tight were his steel boots, after he removed the seven liters of cotton he had stuffed into them. He forgot to unlace his mailed corselet before going to sleep, and it was torn and busted. His golden belt was just long enough now to go around his waist once, and the Lightning-Sword barely reached his knees. He had grown into a giant during his sleep, after drinking from the Milk-Fountain. And the horse, he discovered, was completely healed. He was overjoyed by his amazing transformation. He saddled his horse and galloped off toward the battlefield.

True enough, as he was told, there was an iron tree by the roadside. He drew his sword and cried, "Bread and wine, the living God, Marouta's High Mother of God, the Victory Cross on my right arm!" and smote the iron tree as he swept past it. The keen blade did not break or splinter and he thought he cut through the thick steel of this signpost, but when he glanced back over his shoulder his heart withered in his breast and he gave a loud groan. The iron tree was still standing there, by the roadside. He slowed down and said:

> "Oh, damn it all. I wish I had
> Broken my leg, broken my arm
> Lost my eyesight and not come here
> To this signpost to test my strength.
> If I cannot cut it clean through
> With this great sword, it does not fall,
> Then how can I split Melik's head?"

He felt disgraced before the horse and thought of turning back, but Jalali said: "David, do not despair." A sudden blast of the south wind broke the iron tree in two, where he struck it. He sang out in joyous words:

> "Be strong, my legs, so good of you
> To bring me here; well done, I say.
> Be strong, my arms, be ever green
> And grow in might day after day.
> Be clear, my eyes, shine bright with light
> As you observe this happy scene
> I trust in you in this great fight."

He wheeled around and rode on. Gazing left and right he sang to the rocks and springs, to the trees and mountains of his native land:

> "Farewell O springs of Dzovasar
> When I am parched and you too far
> To slake my thirst, flow on and on
> Never dry up, and make me glad
> With thoughts of you in Egypt's heat.
> Farewell O winds of Dzovasar
> When I feel hot and you too far
> Keep on blowing until we meet.
> O sacred springs and cooling winds
> Flowers and trees, mountains and rocks
> Of my homeland, forget me not."

By nightfall he was on a high mountain-peak overlooking the plain where Misra Melik's armies were drawn up for battle. The blaze of innumerable fires made him pause, and gazing down at the awesome spectacle he thought he could no more count these tents of the enemy than he could count the stars in heaven, or the sands at the seashore. The vast plain swarmed with men and horses. David shook his head in dismay and said in a mournful voice:

"If these were spring lambs, O merciful God
And I a hungry wolf, kill them I could not.
If these were but wool or stacks of dry hay
And I flame and fire, burn them I could not.
If this were just wheat, nothing but millet
And I a reaper, reap them I could not.
If these were ashes and I the south wind
They would still be here — blow them I could not."

The horse did not share David's fears and doubts. He spoke by God's will and said:

"For heaven's sake, David, what are you afraid of? Aren't you Meherr's son? He would never have hesitated to attack. Nothing could frighten your father. These are all earthborn men; you and I are fiery, are we not? I can kill as many of them with my teeth, or feet, or tail, as you can with your sword, or mace, or spear. I will bite their heads off. I will trample them to death. Call upon God and charge."

David kissed his horse, and drew his sword. It flared in the night. "I had better warn them in advance and not take them by surprise," he said. He called out his warning three times:

"Hey-ho! Awake if still asleep
And if awake saddle your mounts
Take up your arms, get on your mounts
Don't say David came like a thief
Sneaked in on you before you woke

And stole away in the dark night.
I want to make this a fair fight."

David kissed the cross of the Holy Mother of God he carried
on his breast, gripped the thunderbolt of Sassoun tighter in his
hand, and charged, shouting "Bread and wine, the living God,
Marouta's High Mother of God, the Victory Cross on my right
arm!" The Egyptians fled in terror. "Is this a man or a demon?"
they said, as he slashed his way through the front ranks and cut
down a thousand men. The bodies of the slain piled up on both
sides of him as he swept across the plain, and his horse killed
as many more, striking them down with his tail, biting off their
legs and arms, cracking their skulls under his feet, trampling
them to death like so many ants. "Run, Jalali, run! Cut, my
sword, cut!" David yelled as they slaughtered the enemy
together.

High up on the mountain pass where the forty tents of Sassoun were pitched, Uncle Toros heard the clamor and tumult
in the plain below, the struggle of men and horses, the blaring
of Arab trumpets and the roll of drums, the cries of the wounded
and dying. He called out to his men, "Boys, great is our God!"
The Sassounians swooped down on Misra Melik's disorganized
army, and caught between David on one side, and Uncle Toros
on the other, the Egyptians and their allies did not know which
way to turn to save their lives and killed one another in the
dark. The massacre continued for three days and nights. The
battlefield ran with blood.

There were smart men among the Arabs. They held a war
council and said: "What shall we do? We shall be slaughtered,
all of us. We have to chain him by catching him off guard."
They threw flaming astragali[3] into the air, and David stopped
to watch their crackling flare filling up the sky. "David, this fire
is pouring down on you from heaven!" they shouted in their despair. "It is a punishment from God. Haven't you killed enough
men? Give up." As David was still watching the flames they

brought up their heavy chains carried by a team of forty buffaloes and tried to capture David and tie him up. David and his horse fought them off before they could draw the chains tightly around them. The slaughter continued, and David's horse waded through torrents of blood carrying off the bodies of the slain Arabs.

There was another wise man among them, an old greybeard, father of seven fighters in Misra Melik's army, who dropped his weapons and ran up to David with a bunch of astragali and feathers[4] on his bare head, crying, "Make way, I want to talk to David, we have to save our men and stop this useless slaughter." They made way for him and he came and bowed to the ground before David. "May God preserve your home, David, the wind made by your horse will knock me over, if you don't stop him. I beg you to listen to me."

David reined in his horse. "What do you wish to tell me, old man?"

"We are not your enemies. We do not hate you, David."

"Then why are you fighting against me?"

"Misra Melik brought us here by force. We did not come of our own will. We too are human beings, and we wish you no harm. All these men you have been slaughtering were born of a father and mother like you. Some of them, can't you see, are still children with smooth beardless faces. Others left their young brides behind them. Many are the bread-winners and sole support of their families. Others have no families, are poor homeless wanderers with no pillow to put their heads on. Don't have the blood of innocent men on your conscience, David. We throw ourselves upon your mercy. Spare us, for God's sake, and put an end to this massacre. Your enemy is the King, your own brother, Misra Melik. Kill the shepherd; the flock is already yours."

"Do you give me your word, as would a Christian, that you mean what you say, that these men don't want to fight against me?"

"I do. By Allah, we will pray for you if you deliver us from our King."

"I pity these poor wretches," David said. "I have no quarrel with them. I believe you, old man. I am looking for Misra Melik. Where is he?"

"Come, I will show you his tent."

David followed the greybeard and the Egyptian troops made way for him with deep salaams and every mark of respect. Among so many other tents it was not easy to find Misra Melik's tent. The old man stood beside it and said: "Here it is. The big green one. With an elephant standing in front and a golden apple glittering on top of the roof. The King has been sitting here in his tent eating roast lamb and pilav and drinking wine while we have been fighting and dying for him. Now I think he is sleeping. That is not smoke, but his own breath, coming out of the tent, and the roof of the tent as you can see goes up and down with every breath he takes. When Misra Melik sleeps forty slave girls kneel around him and rub his feet, and they fan him and keep away the flies."

David dismissed the old warrior. Two Arab spearmen stood guard at the door of the King's tent. David could see the huge mound of Melik's gigantic figure huddled under a quilt inside the tent. Melik was surrounded by his forty slave girls, twenty on each side, rubbing his soles and fanning him with green willow branches. From head to foot Misra Melik was forty arrows long.

David said to the two Arabs at the door: "Wake up your lord if he is asleep and tell him David of Sassoun is waiting for him at the door."

The Arabs said: "We cannot do that, David. When the King sleeps he sleeps for seven days and nights and nobody can wake him up during that time."

"I do not care how long he sleeps, and when he wakes up or does not, I cannot wait to please his moods. This war will go on if he does not come out of his bed and fight me like a man."

Ismil Khatoun came to the door and shrank back in fear and horror when she saw David on his fiery horse, and both spattered with blood.

David said: "Good day, mother."

She said with a forced smile: "David, my sweet boy, welcome, a thousand times welcome! I have missed you so much. Your sight fills my heart with joy and happiness. You were a little boy when you left Egypt, and now you are so big on that big horse that you frighten me. Come in and have breakfast with me. You must be hungry and tired after so much fighting. Take a bath, change your clothes and rest for a while. When your brother wakes up you can talk it over with him and reach a friendly understanding. You can divide the world between you. Let half of the world belong to you, and the other half to Melik. Why fight over it? Come in, don't act like a stranger."

"Thank you, mother, but I am not hungry, I have eaten already. I accepted Melik's challenge and came, and God will give the victory either to me or to him."

This made her angry. "Go away, you mad Daredevil. Have you no sense of gratitude? I nursed you at my breast."

"Melik may be my big brother, but I want you to wake him up, and if he does not come out and meet me like a man I will renew the war."

"He will not get up until he is ready for it, and there is nothing I can do about it. He will sleep for three more days."

"Very well then, I will wake him up myself."

David lost his patience. He dismounted, and before he could tether his horse Jalali bolted and ran up a mountain. The horse did not want him to dismount and was angry with David for not remembering Ohan's warning to stay on his back. David strode into the tent and the slave girls gazed at him with sighs of admiration. They had never seen such a handsome warrior before, and each hoped in her heart David would carry her off and make her his wife.

David stabbed Melik's toes with his father's spear. "Melik, get up. You can sleep later, not for seven days but forever."

Melik stirred under his quilt. "Ouch, my bed is full of bugs."

Melik was just pretending to be asleep.[5] Ismil Khatoun said: "Let him have his sleep, the poor boy."

David said: "Melik, don't give me that old wives' tale about bedbugs. What bit you was my spear." He turned to Ismil Khatoun: "And don't give me a headache with your excuses. Pull him out of bed. I cannot wait."

She heated a plowshare in the fire and held it against his soles. "Ouch! Ouch! Why can't I have a bed without bedbugs, you bitches?" She wanted to frighten David so that he would say: "What a strong man Melik is, she holds a red-hot plowshare against his soles and he thinks it's a bedbug."

"Melik is not sleeping," David said. "He is wide awake under his quilt and can hear everything we say."

"Get up, son. David is here," Ismil Khatoun said.

"David? Who is David?" And Melik turned over under his quilt.

David said: "Just a goatherd and plowman from Sassoun."

Melik sat up in bed, rubbed his eyes, blinked and squinted at David, shading one eye with his left hand and his other eye with his right hand as though David were too small to be visible.

"Take a good look at death's angel," David said. "If you think you are deathless I have brought you death. I have come to claim your soul and send you to deepest hell."

"Death's angel? You are nothing but dog food, you son of a bitch. You had no horse and now you have become a horseman, you are giving yourself big airs as a warrior when I fed you the scraps from my table and you used to lap up my food like a dog. How did you manage to get here? Pretended to be somebody else to fool my soldiers? Get out."

"The man who calls others a son of a bitch is a dog himself. You challenged me, and I came. I came to fight you."

"Fight me? Misra Melik? Who do you think you are?"

"O my little orphan lamb
If I eat you for breakfast
What would I have for my lunch?
And if I eat you for lunch
What would I have for supper?
If I eat you for supper
What is left for next morning?"

David said: "If you can eat me for breakfast, for lunch or for supper, with nothing left for the next day, what are you afraid of then?"

Melik drew in his breath and let it out, as though he could blow David out of his tent. The tent rose and staggered in the wind made by his breath, but David stood firm before Melik, and said: "Your troops have laid down their arms and there is no one to fight me now except you. This is the day, Melik, this is the day. The divinity will decide between us and give the victory either to me or to you!"

The strength of forty buffaloes drained away from the King. He grinned and said: "The devil take you, Lisping David, if you came to my tent to fight me, there is plenty of time for fighting. Sit down and make yourself at home. Let us have something to eat, I would enjoy having a chat with you. Why be in such a hurry?"

"We do not break bread with our enemies."

"David, I am still sleepy. If you must fight, come back tomorrow."

David said: "I will be back tomorrow."

He pitched his little tent near Misra Melik's and lay down to sleep. His feet stuck out of the tent. A servant came to him the next morning and invited him to be the King's guest. "I have forty-year-old pomegranate wine," Misra Melik said in his message. The wine tempted him. Melik met him before the green tent, with his sword slung from his shoulder and a large cross hanging on his breast. "Let us reconcile," he said. "But if you still insist on fighting, let us eat and drink together, and then fight."

"If I do not eat and drink with him he will think I am afraid," David thought, entering the tent.

Rugs were spread before the royal tent and David was received formally as the King's guest. He was led into the tent by Melik and was served forty-year-old wine, while the King himself drank new wine. Suddenly the rug under him gave way and David fell into a well forty cubits deep. He was caught in an intricate net of iron rings and chains, and the steel trapdoor closed over him. Melik brought millstones and piled them up on top of the well. He laughed. "Ha! Ha! Ha! David of Sassoun came to fight with me! Our Lisping David had the courage to stand up against the King of Egypt. Let him stay there until his bones rot. Let him die like a dog!" He spat.

Night fell. Melik slept in his comfortable bed and David was in the well befuddled by the wine and struggling in vain to free himself from the iron rings and chains that wound tighter with every movement he made.

Back in Sassoun, Uncle Ohan woke up his wife and said: "Get up, David is in trouble. I just dreamt it was bright sunlight in Egypt, dark and misty in Sassoun."

Sara said: "Homewrecker, let me have some sleep. Do you sleep for yourself and dream for David?"

Ohan slept some more, and saw another dream. He shook her again. "Wife, get up, I am afraid we lost David. I dreamt the star of Egypt was very bright, the star of Sassoun very pale. David showed his mettle, and it is now up to me to do something for him."

Sara said: "May God wreck your home, man, go to sleep."

Uncle Ohan woke her up for the third time. "Wife, get up, I said, they must have murdered David. I dreamt the star of Egypt swallowed up the star of Sassoun."

He kicked her. "You are a foreign woman, Sara, and your heart does not grieve like mine for David. Get up and bring me my clothes and arms."

Sara got out of bed and lit the lamp. She brought him his clothes and arms. Ohan watched David's star from the roof of his house and saw that it was so dim it was dying out, as he had dreamt. He went to the stable and opened the door. His horses were very restless and excited, kicking and trying to get out of their stalls. He put his hand on the back of the White Horse, and it caved in. He said: "White horse, how soon can you take me to David?"

The horse said: "Give me a measure of barley and we will be there by noon."

Uncle Ohan struck him and said: "I have been feeding you for nothing. Am I going to reach David or his corpse by noon?"

He laid his hand on his Red horse, and the belly of the Red horse went down, too, and Ohan said: "Hey, Red horse, when can you take me to David?"

"Give me two measures of barley and we will be there by the time the sun warms up."

"By the time the sun warms up David will be dead."

Ohan laid his hand on his Black horse. The Black horse did not go down. Ohan kissed him on the head.

"Black horse, how soon can you take me to David if I feed you three measures of barley?"

"God willing, with three measures of barley we will be there by the time both of your feet are in my stirrups."

The Black horse was a fiery horse.

"Wife," Ohan said, "bring me my seven buffalo-hides and seven plow-chains."

Sara brought them to him. Ohan mounted his Black horse and was on the mountain-top near Lera-plain in the twinkling of an eye. He tried his strength by ripping up a poplar tree. "I can still do it," he said. He wrapped himself tightly in his seven buffalo-hides, and threw the plow-chains around his shoulders and chest so that he would not explode when he shouted in his thundering voice:

"Hey, David, where are you? Do you hear me? You forgot to say your prayer, the devil take you, or did your tongue dry up in your mouth? Say, for God's sake, Bread and wine, the living God, Marouta's High Mother of God, the Victory Cross on my right arm, and shake yourself."

David heard him. "Hey-hey, this is Uncle Ohan's voice. He is calling me. I was so confused when I fell into this well I forgot to pray. Yeah,[6] Bread and wine, yeah, the living God, yeah, Marouta's High Mother of God, the Victory Cross on my right arm." He shook himself. And instantly, by God's order, the chains and iron rings broke, the millstones cracked and splintered and rose sky-high, and anyone who was hit by one of the flying pieces was killed on the spot. David sprang out of the well and confronted Melik.

"So this is how you entertain me as your guest. You will not fool me again."

Melik said: "I wanted to be sure you will not run away from me until we fought in single combat, so I kept you in the well."

"We shall see who is afraid. Come out of this tent and fight like a man."

Uncle Ohan called out from the mountain-top: "David, come here!"

"I will be back," David said to Melik, and ran up the mountain to his uncle. He found Uncle Ohan on his Black horse, wrapped in his buffalo-hides and plow-chains, with a great poplar tree on his shoulder. Not far from him was Jalali.

"David, when I saw your horse without you I thought they had murdered you already. Jalali heard me and came neighing loudly, but I still don't dare go near him."

Jalali ran up to David with a joyous whinny, and David put his arms around his neck and caressed and kissed him.

"Uncle Ohan, you can go home now. I have stopped the slaughter and will fight Misra Melik in single combat."

"Don't you ever forget to say your prayers again and call on
Marouta's High Mother of God when you are in trouble."

Ohan returned to Sassoun and David raced down the mountain to Melik's tent. Seeing him back on his horse, with one hand
gripping his mace, Melik said: "David my soul, you want to fight
me when I brought singers and dancers for your wedding."

"Still trying to fool me. Get ready, let's go to the arena
and let God choose between us."

Misra Melik ordered that his fiery horse be brought to him.
He did not eat or drink. He dressed up and slung on his arms.
He mounted, and they rode out to the arena at the camp. The
troops stood around and shouted their approval of the single
combat. "May the better man win!" The old greybeard saved
a hundred thousand men, and they favored David, wanted to
serve him, not Misra Melik.

As the fighting stopped Uncle Toros came up with his thirty-
eight mounted warriors from the other end of the battlefield and
told David, "Well done, my boy."

David and Misra Melik rode around the arena, warming up
their horses. Melik said: "David, shall we fight in free style,
or by turn?"

"As you like."

"By turn then. Each man is allowed three strikes. Who shall
strike first?"

"You are the challenger, but you strike first. You are older.
And if you kill me, Melik, I have no mother or wife or sister
to weep over me and to bury me."

Ismil Khatoun came up and said to Melik:

> "I saw again a fearful dream
> The moon was bright over Sassoun
> Dark in Egypt. Don't fight David
> No good I say will come of it."

Misra Melik pondered this new warning and said: "David killed
too many of my men, mother."

"Come, son, let's go back to Egypt."

"I have brought almost the whole world here, how can I go back now without settling this issue once and for all? It would be impossible for me to reign in Egypt if I do not fight David and wipe out the Armenians. I will kill Uncle Toros too, and Uncle Ohan. Fool David thinks he will survive three strikes by me."

Misra Melik played with his mace, weighing three hundred and sixty liters. He swung it to the left, to the right, and twelve liters of fiery sparks poured out of it. David shouted: "Melik, strike! I will wait for your first strike here."

Melik rode all the way to Diyarbekir and came back thundering across the plain while David waited on his horse, covering himself with his shield, one hand on Marouta's holy emblem, and murmuring a prayer. Melik yelled in a fierce voice, "Dust you are, and to dust you return," and struck with savage fury. His mace cracked the earth wide open and sounded like forty pairs of buffaloes dragging a plow. David disappeared in storm clouds of dust and the King sighed in a mock voice: "Alas, a thousand times alas, our splendid David was dust and I turned him to dust." He waited until the dust-storm settled, and heard David shout back:

"Don't worry, Melik, I haven't turned to dust yet." His fiery horse flew up and Melik missed him.

Melik said: "Homewrecker, I did not go far enough. I will strike again."

He turned his horse around and rode to Aleppo. He came like a flash and let David have it. The earth groaned. Melik drove his mace forty cubits into the ground, but missed David, whose horse sprang up again, and David disappeared in the duststorm Melik stirred up over the world. The King lamented: "Alas, a thousand times alas, we reared splendid David in our home, we took care of him as our very own, and now we lost him. The poor darling turned to dust."

David said, as the air cleared: "Melik, be sure you don't miss the third time. It is your last strike."

"Hey! You still alive?" The world whirled darkly around him. "David, my brother, this is enough for today. We can continue tomorrow."

"No, strike now," David said.

"You stand here, then, and don't move." Melik made him change his position. He thought he had to go even farther to strike harder. He blamed it all on his horse. He rode to Baghdad[7] and came back at unimaginable speed to send David to the bottomless pit. He struck, and the whole world shook as in an earthquake. He tore the sky apart, as when stormclouds in the spring flare up on mountain-tops during a cracking roll of thunder. The sun was blotted out. Nothing could be seen for a day and night, and Melik lamented: "Alas, a thousand times alas, our splendid David was dust, and I turned him to dust." When the duststorm settled and the sun came out David slapped his head a few times to straighten up his neck, which was bent to one side.

"Don't worry, Melik, I am still here."

"Hey, homewrecker, let me try once more," Melik said.

"No, you had three chances. Now it is my turn. Which do you prefer? My sword or my mace?"

Melik said in his mind: "Who can stand a blow by his mace?" He called out: "David, strike with your sword. But give me seven hours to prepare for it."

"You can have forty hours if you like. Go dig up your grave and have your tombstone carved."

"I fear that look in your eyes, David. Will you let me wait for your first strike in my tent? I will go lie down in my tent."

"Go lie down wherever you like, and if you are so scared go down to the bottom of the well and close its mouth with forty millstones and forty buffalo-hides. I have three strikes."

"Your fiery horse leaped high into the clouds when I struck

and that's why I missed. To make this a fair contest I will go stay in the well."

They lowered Misra Melik into the well, forty cubits deep, and closed its mouth with forty millstones and forty buffalo-hides, and then spread carpets and his quilt over it. Melik felt safe in the well. David mounted his horse and raced back to Dzovasar. He came flying with the Lightning-Sword blazing in his hand. Ismil Khatoun ran and stopped him before the tent by baring her bosom.

"David, spare him your first strike for the sake of the sweet milk you sucked at my breast."

David lowered his sword, raised it to his lips, kissed it, touched his forehead with it. "Mother, you did not ask Melik to spare me his first strike, but the first strike is yours."

David wheeled around, and then came storming down from the mountains of Sassoun. Melik's sister ran up and stopped him just before he reached the green tent. "David, when you were a little boy I carried you on my back, I held you in my lap, I washed your diapers, I loved you like your own sister. Don't strike your second strike for my sake."

David said: "Sister, you did not hold Melik back when he struck me three times with his mace, but I will give up my second strike." He lowered his sword, raised it to his lips, kissed it, touched his forehead with it, and said: "Only one left, and this last strike belongs to God."

David wheeled around and was off again to the mountains of Armenia. Ismil Khatoun ordered the young brides and the un-married girls she brought with her to line up before the tent. She said: "Quick, play your fiddles! Quick, play your pipes! And beat your drums! Wave your silk handkerchiefs and dance, dance for him! David is a hot-blooded single man, he will look at you and miss his last strike."

The girls belly-danced and sang *Janiman*.[8] David kept his wits about him. "One God, one David, one strike." He said his profession of faith, "I believe . . . " and struck the green tent like a thunderbolt shot out of Mount Ararat. He cut through forty millstones, he cut through forty buffalo-hides, he split Melik's skull in two and his sword came out between the legs of the monster and plunged forty cubits into the very bowels of the earth where the black waters flow. If an angel had not held his arm David would have flooded the whole earth with the black waters of the bottomless pit.

Misra Melik called from the depths of the well: "David, that was just a flea bite. Strike again. And hurry. It's cold down here."

David said: "Melik, shake yourself, move around a bit. A brave man strikes only once."

Melik shook himself. One half of him fell to one side of the well, the other half fell to the other side, and that was the end of the King of Egypt.

David said to Ismil Khatoun: "Mother, open the well and let me see what happened to Melik."

She said: "You go away. We will open it."

He went away, but came back and watched them remove the quilt and the carpets he had cut through, the forty millstones he had cut through, the forty buffalo-hides he had cut through, and when the well was opened he leaned over his horse and peered down. He called: "Melik, Melik, Melik!" There was no answer. "Come out of the well," the others said. Still no answer. A rope was lowered into the well and a slave girl slid down. She found only the right half of the King's body. The other half, his left side, disappeared in the black waters. When the right half was drawn up Misra Melik's mother, his sister and his wife sat by the well and wept over it. David kissed his glittering sword and drove it back into the scabbard.

He put this right half of Melik's body on his horse and had it buried on a high place by the Christian rite. "This is my father's half," he said. After her loud wails, Ismil Khatoun dried her eyes and turning to David said: "What is done is done. You

killed him, but you too are my son. Come, David, marry Melik's wife and be King of Egypt. Sassoun is already yours."

David said: "I was born without a blemish, of pure Christian stock, and I intend to remain so. It would be unlawful to marry a pagan woman."

She lifted her head and said in an angry voice: "David, you left Melik's young wife a widow and may your own wife become a widow before her time."

David said: "Mother, let me take you to Sassoun with me. From now on you can live with me."

"No, David, I will never come to Sassoun. Not after you killed your brother."

He asked that Misra Melik's son Khosrov be brought to him. He himself girt the young boy with the sword and made him King of Egypt.[9]

David commanded that all the remaining troops assemble before him. They kissed his hands and feet as they gathered in the arena. Seated on his great horse, David said to them:

"I give you permission to return to your homes. Go back, and give blessings to my father and mother. I will not punish any-one for fighting against me. Let us live in peace. But I warn you that if you break the peace I am imposing upon you and invade my country again you will not be able to save your lives even if you hide in wells forty cubits deep under forty millstones and forty buffalo-hides. You would have to reckon with this sword that strikes lightning. You would have to reckon with David of Sassoun."

"David of Sassoun!" the troops shouted as if with one voice. "May we die for your head and sun, may God be with you, may God give you long life, may he deem your father and mother worthy of paradise. We shall bless you in our hearts as long as we live."

They passed under his sword before returning to their own cities and lands.

A proud-looking Commander rode up to David, with whip

in hand, and said: "David, my brother, thank you for sparing
my army. Since both of us are single I propose a pact of per-
petual friendship between us."

"Who are you? Where are you from?" David asked.

"I am Pajik, King of the East. David, we shall marry some
day. If you have a son and I have a daughter let your son marry
my daughter. If you have a daughter and I a son let my son
marry your daughter."

They swore an oath and the King of the East departed with
his army, as did the remnants of the other armies, singing
David's praises as they scattered to the four corners of the earth.
Ismil Khatoun also took her army and went back to Egypt,
which David returned to her as a tributary of Sassoun.

David and Uncle Toros and his thirty-eight warriors turned
their horses around and rode back to Sassoun with nothing but
an ox cart.[10] David had Misra Melik's ear stuck at the end of his
spear to give it to Vergo and his wife. As they reached the
approaches of Sassoun the guards on the watchtowers of the
citadel saw a lone horseman followed by thirty-nine other horsemen and decided it could not be Misra Melik's army coming
up the road, these horsemen were too few, not the countless
hordes of Egypt they expected to see through clouds of dust.
A scout ran to Uncle Ohan with the good news. And soon the
entire population of the city, men, women, children, the young
and old, led by Uncle Ohan, hurried with lutes and drums and
bagpipes to meet the returning warriors. When David saw them
coming down the road and recognized his own countrymen he
yelled: "Uncle Ohan, are you coming against me with an army
bigger than Melik's?"

Ohan thundered: "Thank God you came back to us safe and
sound. All these people have been praying for you. They were
afraid the Arabs would be marching up this road to kill our
men and carry off our women and children."

David and his uncle embraced each other. "Go back, go
back," David said. "I killed Misra Melik."

Ohan wiped his brow. "Glory be to God. We have nothing to fear any more. Sassoun is free."

"Aunt Sara," David said. "You wanted Misra Melik's ear. Here it is."

They took David home like a king. He bathed and changed his bloody clothes. They washed his horse and groomed him before they tied him in the stall, and gave him all the barley he could eat. Sassoun honored David with a glorious victory feast that lasted seven days. The minstrels sang, they ate and drank, they danced, there were fireworks. Golden-Braids came out of her room, and now that her wish came true and David succeeded his father she could enjoy the sunlight, and celebrations like this feast, instead of staying behind seven locked doors in mourning as she had done for years. Barav said to David: "Welcome home, David. Welcome, welcome! You see? Misra Melik was not a man to fight with a rusty pocket knife or with a poplar tree." David said: "Thank you, Mamik, for your advice."

"More wine!" David shouted. He raised the wine bowl with seven handles to his mouth and drank it down, to the last drop. Then he lay down to sleep for three days and nights.

Uncle Ohan said: "God lit the firelight of Sassoun. With David back victorious, the whole world belongs to me. I think it is time for David to marry. I have to find a good wife for our boy. What do you say, my friends? Does this meet with your approval?"

And the princely men at the feast, the great chieftains, nodded and said: "Why not? We are all for it, Ohan. Let the liberator of Sassoun marry the girl of his choice."

NOTES

[1] Evidently the sword remained rustproof in pitch, which is waterproof, and Meherr kept his sword in a large jar filled with pitch because no one could pull it out. David does, as though pulling a hair out of dough.

[2] Ohan's wife (or Vergo's wife) asks David to bring him Melik's left testis "as a remedy for sore eyes." There are many allusions to it in rough peasant humor.

[3] Astragali: a thorny mountain bush called *gaz* that grows close to the ground and is used as kindling or firewood. *Astragalus tragacanthe.*

[4] Evidently feathers or astragali or both were worn on the head by messengers or runners in time of war.

[5] Melik pretends to be asleep: DS vol. I, pp. 432-33. In other variants, he is actually asleep.

[6] Yeah also in the original texts.

[7] These cities or places have no real connection with this episode but are mentioned to indicate distances, "in a manner of speaking," as one reciter explains.

[8] *Janiman*: a popular song.

[9] Khosrov: DS, vol. I, p. 1063. A common name among Armenians and Iranians, and evidently an allusion to Chosroes I and Chosroes II, two famous Sassanian kings, who fought wars in Armenia.

[10] It may be that the ox cart carried Misra Melik's right, Christian side for burial in Sassoun. This is suggested by the wording in some variants.

DAVID AND THE LADY KHANDOUT

ALL LOOKED UP to David after this victorious war. He was no longer a homeless orphan whose word did not carry much weight in Sassoun. He came back from the war a changed man. He filled out, he became a mighty giant, and any woman who saw his beautiful eyes, his red cheeks, his fine nose, mouth and features, went crazy over him.

"Mamik, I have no mother," he said to Barav. "Will you come and live with me as my mother?"

She said: "David, I am already your mother. I do not have to live with you to keep you informed of what is going on. When there is any news I will come and tell you. From now on you have nothing to worry about. Flourish, prosper, enjoy life. You are no longer a fool, but a sensible young man."

"Ask Ohan," she said, "to have your father's hall made ready for you. Live in your father's hall. You will find Meherr's chests standing there. Fold your father's clothes and keep them in his chests, and hang your sword on the wall with your own hands. You need a groom for your horse, and another man to walk in front of you and to carry out your orders. Well, David, I had better be on my way."

David went to Uncle Ohan and said: "Uncle Ohan, open my father's hall and throw down plenty of mattresses and cushions for my guests. From now on I will live in my father's hall."

"Certainly," said Ohan. "Why shouldn't you? I will have everything ready for you. With the firelight of Sassoun burning so brightly again we can smile and laugh and rejoice in our freedom. I am so happy!"

Ohan cleaned and tidied up Meherr's hall and made it look elegant. Nothing was good enough for David. David moved in, and said: "Uncle Ohan, you are like my own father. I will not let you bring me food and drink. You are not my servant. Get a man to do such chores, and get another man to take care of my horse. Pay them well."

Every evening for the next few weeks the princes of Sassoun gathered in David's hall. They came to converse with him and pay him homage as the liberator of Sassoun.

One night Uncle Ohan was asleep in his bedroom. His wife Sara got up and, secretly, baked sugared bread. She cooked a chicken. She took honey, butter, seven-year-old wine. She wore her prettiest clothes, painted her eyes, dressed her hair, with her braids hanging out from under her headdress on both sides of her face, put on her very pretty boots, lighted a candle, and went on tiptoe to David's hall. He closed his door before going to bed, and was asleep when she said:

"David, open the door."

He said: "Who is it?"

"Your Uncle Ohan's wife."

He got up and opened the door. She entered his room and sat down.

"David," she said, "I have missed you. I did not see you for so long, and was unable to bring you delicacies like these. I prepared them for you."

She opened her basket, and put a jar of wine and a cup

before David. He thought to himself: "I have no mother and she wants to mother me."

He thanked her and said: "Aunt Sara, you have been like a mother to me, and now you are doing me this honor."

"David, may I be your sacrifice, there never was a hero like you in Sassoun, and there never will be."

He ate the good things she brought him, drank the pomegranate wine. Well, he was David. He drank too much. His head dropped on a cushion and he fell asleep.

While he slept Ohan's wife kissed him on his cheeks, on his forehead. Then she got up and went to her own room. Ohan was still in bed sleeping.

Every night, for a whole week, Sara visited David, and every night David fell asleep while she was with him. She said to herself: "Why should I take him seven-year-old wine? He drinks it and falls asleep. What do I get for it? Nothing." So she took him only a year-old wine, and not too much of it. He stayed awake this time. She got up and sat in his lap. She flung her arms around his neck and wanted to kiss him on his cheeks. He pushed her away, he would not let her kiss him. He said: "You have taken my mother's place. You go sit over there. You do not have to sit on my lap to talk to me."

She said: "David, how can you say I have taken your mother's place? Don't you know I am a foreign girl who came here to marry your uncle?"

"My uncle's wife is the same as my mother to me, and as dear as the moon-and-the-sun."

"David, I told you I am a foreign woman. I have been living with your uncle all these years, but I do not love him. I don't want him any more. I want you."

David sat there thinking: "If I strike her and kill her my uncle will say I murdered his wife. If I don't kill her, she will be pestering me and will not leave me alone."

"Aunt Sara," he said, "you go now and let me have my sleep. We will talk it over tomorrow." He got rid of her.

Early the next morning David got up and went to wash at the public fountain. He sat down by the fountain thinking, thinking, when Barav made her appearance. He said with a motion of his hand: "Mamik, come here." She came over, and he told her everything Ohan's wife did and said.

"Mamik, you are like my own mother, that is why I am telling you everything."

Barav said: "David, I cannot really blame Ohan's wife for what she did. You are not a child any more. You are past twenty, and still unmarried. Any woman who sees you wants to crawl to bed with you."

"Well, Mamik, what shall I do?"

"Go get yourself a wife, so that women will leave you alone. They take one look at your handsome figure and go crazy. Yes, David, there are such things in this world. I did not want to tell you before. Marry a good and beautiful girl, one worthy of you."

"Mamik, you find me a wife. I don't know how to go about it."

"David, Khandout Khatoun is the woman for you."

"Who is Khandout Khatoun? Where does she live?"

"She is a Persian princess in Tabriz, as brave and as good-looking as you are. A lovely pahlevan."

"Mamik, can you tell me how to go to Tabriz?"

"Ask the way to Akhlat. When you get to Akhlat ask the way to Bergri. When you get to Bergri ask the way to Khoy. When you get to Khoy ask the way to Tabriz."

David's fame spread to all parts of the world and Khandout Khatoun heard about his strength in Tabriz. One day she was sitting at her window when she saw three minstrels passing by with their lutes slung from their shoulders. She called them: "Minstrels, come here!" She asked them: "How much do you earn a day?"

They said: "Lady, our earnings are uncertain. Sometimes we earn a silver coin a day, sometimes two silver coins. Sometimes more, sometimes less."

She gave them a handful of gold coins and said: "Go sing before David, praising me. Maybe he will come and marry me, but may he turn into stone if he does not. God be with you."

The whole world knew of the beauty of Khandout Khatoun. Her loveliness shone like the sun. The Shah of Iran wanted her for himself. The great pahlevan Lorva Hamza demanded Khandout be given to him. The King of Chin-ma-Chin, the Black King, the King of Khurasan, Oghan, Toghan, all wanted to marry Khandout. Other bold champions, forty in number, from forty kingdoms, each confident in his own strength, were at her doorstep as suitors, eating and drinking at their own expense, hoping she would consent to marry one of them. But Khandout Khatoun said in her mind: "If there is one man for me, it is David. What are these others compared to David? Why should I even bother with them?"

The three minstrels first went to Egypt by way of Aleppo. There were weavers from Sassoun and many other Armenians in Egypt and the minstrels sang the lays of Sassoun and Moush in the market-place, but they were told David, the conqueror of Egypt, was in Sassoun, and they came to Sassoun, strum-strumming their lutes. Children playing in the streets followed them. They had never heard such sweet tuneful sounds coming out of a piece of hollow wood with an ear at the end.

The minstrels asked the children: "Where is David's hall?"

The children took them to David's house. He was not at home. He was hunting in Dzovasar. The minstrels said to Uncle Ohan: "We came to praise Khandout Khatoun to David."

He said: "Praise her to me."

They took him for David, sat before him and struck their lutes, holding them on their knees.

"Minstrels, whose daughter is Khandout Khatoun? Where does she live?" Ohan asked.

"She is the daughter of the Lord of Tabriz, lives in Iran."

"Get out of here!" Uncle Ohan broke their lutes over their heads and gave them a terrible beating. "Go, tell Khandout. Go back where you came from."

The minstrels ran, crying and cursing.

Ohan said: "They came to deceive David with their lies. He is innocent like a deer. I don't want my boy to marry a pagan lady."

The minstrels stopped under the city bridge and wondered if they said something wrong to make David so angry. Soon David saw them on his way home from Dzovasar, his spear and horse loaded with wild sheep, wild boars, and other game. They hung out like branches of a tree. He heard them cursing him, his parents, his dead.

"Hey, men, why are you cursing me?"

"We are not cursing *you*. We are cursing that madman David. We are minstrels, and we came to sing the praises of Khandout Khatoun to David. He broke our lutes over our heads, beat us up, ordered us out of town. May God wreck his home and shorten his life."

"That was my uncle, minstrels. The man you are looking for is myself. I am David. Come, sing your praises to me. Let's see what she is like."

"We cannot sing without our lutes." They showed him their broken instruments.

"Go get yourselves new lutes and come to my hall. Put gold strings on them." He gave each man three gold coins.

They thanked him. They came to his hall with their new lutes, sat before him. The first to sing was a graybeard, who tuned his instrument, and struck up this song:

> "If about her whiteness you want to know
> She is whiter than the purest spring snow

If about her softness you want to know
She is like a big soft cotton pillow
If about her fair hair you want to know
She has forty braids, plus one, I vow.
In stature she is like a lakeshore reed
To David I praise my Khandout Khatoun
Her heart is so big it's made for your steed
To gallop in it at a reckless speed
To David I praise my Khandout Khatoun
The taste of her lips is like heaven's mead
To David I praise my Khandout Khatoun
She has pearls for teeth, her breath is rose-sweet
To David I praise my Khandout Khatoun
When you lift her veil she ravishes the heart
Her sight drives you mad, you sigh and you swoon
And she longs to see David of Sassoun
The light of her eyes, her life and her sun.
David, heed her call, Khandout is afire
Khandout burns for you with love and desire."

David liked it very much and said: "Thank you, master."
Next, the darkbeard took up his lute, kissed it, tuned it, and
praised Khandout Khatoun in this manner:

"I turn look at her, she is a picture drawn by a master's quill
        Ah, a master's quill!
I turn look at her, eyes like Chinese cups filled with
                                            heady wine
        Ah, with heady wine!
I turn look at her, polished are her nails and arched her
                                            dark brows
        Ah, arched her dark brows!
I turn look at her, forty fragrant braids crown her lovely head
        Ah, her lovely head!
I turn look at her, her height and figure are a city's tower
        Ah, she is a tower!

I turn look at her, her cheeks turn crimson like pomegranate
bloom
  Ah, pomegranate bloom!
I turn look at her, her bosom is packed with Aleppo sweets
Ah, Khandout's bosom!"

David said: "Thank you, master," and turned to the beardless
young minstrel. "Now let me see what your lute has to say."
  He tuned it and sang:

"If I tell you about her height, it's forty measures and then
  one more
  If I tell you about her heart, it's seven measures and then
  one more
  If I tell you about her neck, it's two palms long and then
  one more
  If I tell you of her lashes, they are the wings of a heron
  If I tell you about her breasts, she is a soft cotton cushion
  If I tell you of her whiteness, she is as white as one-day
  snow
  If I tell you about her voice it sounds sweeter than any lute
  She is a treasure, men's idol, such is my good Lady Khandout."

David thanked him and reached for his own lute. He tuned it
and sang his response:

"Welcome, O minstrels. My heart till today
Was unsullied milk, you came curdled it.
My heart was as clear as a stream in the fall
You came and stirred it, you muddied it all
You made it a flood rising in the spring.
My heart was as strong as Sassoun's grim fort
You came and wrecked it, razed it to the ground.
An innocent lamb changed to a hungry wolf
That is how I feel after all you said
I have no more peace, and I feel I found
The girl of my choice. O minstrels, you came

And with your words and songs set my soul on fire

This fairy-like lady is my heart's desire."

When he finished David put down his lute and asked: "How far is Tabriz?"

"It would take us seven days to get back."

"Tell her I will wait six days, and will be her guest on the seventh day."

He gave them a cupful of gold coins, kept them for supper, and early the next morning the minstrels started out for Tabriz, strum-strumming their strings.

David went to Uncle Ohan and said: "I believe the minstrels told me the truth about Khandout Khatoun. I cannot eat or drink thinking of her. I am love-sick, and there is only one cure for this ailment — marry her. I shall die if she does not become my bride."

"David, forty pahlevans have been sitting at her door for seven years. She is wanted by many kings. If she gives you a sign of encouragement, stay. If not, don't waste your time, come back. I will find a beautiful wife for you."

Uncle Toros said: "I am afraid you will get hurt."

David said: "I will not be a man if I refuse. My going is in my hands, my return in God's. Remember me in your prayers."

Six days later David opened his father's chests, wore his best clothes, girt on his sword, led his horse out of the stable, saddled him, mounted, and was off to Khandout's city, flying between heaven and earth.

Two pahlevans stopped him on the bridge at Akhlat. "Who are you?"

"I am David of Sassoun."

"Welcome to our city, David of Sassoun. You are expected at the King's palace, where a feast has been prepared for you."

Akhlat was a Turkish city. The pahlevans took him to the palace and tied his horse in the royal stable. David sat down, waiting for the King, but instead of the King a woman came in. He stood up. "Where is the King?" he asked.

"I am the King," said Chimishkik Sultana. "The King died and I rule in his stead. David, I want you to be my guest today, and eat with me before you go."

She went crazy over David. After he finished eating, he said: "Bring my horse, I have to go."

She said: "It is late, getting dark, stay here tonight."

"No, impossible, I have to go."

"David, I know where you are going. Khandout Khatoun is not worth my little finger. You believe the minstrels? It is all lies. There can be no such woman in this world. You have been deceived and I fear something dreadful will happen to you. Come, marry me. I am a good woman, the widow of a King, and King in my own right. My kingdom and everything I own will be yours."

David was an ardent young man and did not care whether she was a Turkish or Armenian lady, and Chimishkik Sultana was a sorceress. She bathed him, she wined him and dined him, she made the bed, and crawled to bed with him. They exchanged rings.[1]

He was sorry the next morning. "Woe to me, what did I do?" he said to himself. "Lose my mind? Our nation should not be deceived, but I was deceived by this woman."

While the queen was still in bed, David led his horse out of her stable and rode out of Akhlat without having breakfast. Chimishkik Sultana said, when she saw he was gone: "Wait, you will pay for this."

On reaching Bergri, with its rich farmlands, David ran into a team of seven plows. He saw that the buffaloes had their tongues hanging from the heat.

He said: "Good day to you, and success, brother plowmen."

They said: "God's day, traveler."

"Plowing on a warm day like this, in a dry field, is hard on buffaloes. Let them rest in the river, under those poplars, and I will plow up this field myself."

He dismounted, unyoked the buffaloes and led them to the river. "Don't be angry with me," he said to the leader of the team. "You rest, too." He tied the plow chains to the stirrups of his horse, and rode around the field, and up and down the hill, seven times.

One of the men said: "That was your horse's trick."

David jumped off his horse, tied the plowchains around his arms, and dragged all seven plows after him, going round and round and up and down the hill. The whole field was black, plowed up in an hour. They watched him with their mouths open.

David said: "Well, brothers, I will be on my way."

They said: "It is already noon. Eat with us and then go."

"Give my portion to your children. If I eat with you nothing will be left for them."

"We brought enough food to last us a week. There is plenty to eat. A plowman does not go hungry. The world's prosperity depends on the plow."

David washed his horse in the river, washed off his own dirt and sweat, and came and sat down with his brother plowmen. He was famished. His horse grazed near him. They brought a great four-liter platter of pilav and a stack of thin sheets of bread and placed them before him. David fell on the food, cleaned up the platter and ate all the bread before the others had a bite to eat. They brought him seven sacks of bread, all they had, and he did not leave them a crumb.

"The devil take him, he ate it all, and will eat us too," the men said among themselves. "Nobody would believe it."

"Brothers, your work is finished, you can take up your plows and go home now," David said. "Stack them up, with all your tools, and I will show you another trick."

He stacked them up and said in his mind: "If I can drive my sword through all these plows, I shall marry Khandout Khatoun. If I fail, I had better turn back." He drew his sword, called on Marouta's High Mother of God, and struck, smashing all seven plows to pieces, and driving his sword a cubit into the ground. He flung to the astounded plowmen a fistful of gold coins. "Go get yourselves new plows."

They asked him: "Hey, traveler, are you by any chance the man they call David of Sassoun?"

"I am that man."

"David, there never was and there never will be another champion like you. Wherever you go, may you never stumble on a rock. May you never have an evil day. May you always stay green. May God be always with you."

"Thank you, brothers. Goodbye."

He rode off on his thundering horse. "Iran, where are you, I am coming!"

The minstrels were back in Tabriz on the seventh day. Khandout was seated at her window. She asked them: "Did you see David?" They said: "Lady, may God wreck their homes, they are all madmen in Sassoun. We went to David's house and sang your praises, and we got a beating for it. From Uncle Ohan. Then we met David by the city bridge — may God give him long life. David received us kindly in his hall. He said: 'Go tell Khandout Khatoun I will wait six days and be her guest on the seventh day.'"

She paid them off, each man receiving his weight in gold. "For your children," she said.

She waited anxiously for David. Toward evening she saw whirling clouds of dust darken the sky. Her maids said: "That must be your Daredevil coming from Sassoun." Khandout could barely make out the figure of a horseman flying like a streak of fire between heaven and earth. She said: "Gorgiz, there is no telling what a man of Sassoun might do. Close the gate." The words were still in her mouth when David pulled up under her window. She was so happy to see him — he was seven times more handsome than she imagined him to be — that she threw him an apple. He caught it as it struck him on the heart. He looked at her apple and laughed. She disappeared behind her window.

He rode on to the gate of her garden-palace. He saw a huge man standing before it with a mace in his hand, one lip turned up, another lip reaching down to his chin, a demon with black paws. So odd and frightful was the man's appearance that David said in his mind: "I have never greeted a man from fear, but this demon could kill me, swallow me up with his lips if I do not salute him." He called out: "Good day, pahlevan," and was sorry as soon as he said it. The gate-keeper returned his salute, gripped David's hand with his black paws.

David asked: "What's your name, pahlevan?"

"Gorgiz."

"I am David of Sassoun."

"I know."

David said:

> "Never before in all my life
> Have I greeted a man from fear
> And here I meet this man Gorgiz
> And am so scared as I draw near
> I let him hold my hand in his."

Gorgiz said:

> "For seven years I guard this gate
> Without ever greeting a man
> But when David stands before me
> I shake inside, I dread this man,
> And say to him, Welcome, my mate."

David said: "Blessed is our merciful God. If you had not returned my greeting from fear, as I myself greeted you from fear, I would have died of remorse. Gorgiz, when I marry Khandout Khatoun will you be the godfather of my children?"

"I'll be glad to, David."

"What's that club they have put in your hand? Let me see it."

Gorgiz handed it to him. David threw it away, and that mace it still going . . .

"Godfather Gorgiz, take my horse to the stable."

"David, the stable is full. There isn't room for another horse."

"My horse will make room for himself. Whose horses are they?"

"Khandout Khatoun's suitors', royal sons, from forty kingdoms. There isn't a single empty stall left."

David rode into the yard and dismounted before the stable. He unsaddled his horse, took off the bridle, and said: "Go in, Jalali. If you become the master of all these horses, I will be the master of their owners."

The horse ran into the stable with a loud joyous whinney, and pushed, bit, kicked the other horses, and drove them all into a corner. He went through their stalls and ate all the barley and hay in their mangers. Servants ran to Khandout Khatoun and said: "David's horse proved his mettle. Now it is David's turn to prove his."

"Godfather Gorgiz, let's go in, I am hungry."

Gorgiz led him into the hall, where the forty strongmen were enjoying a feast. Their swords hung on the wall behind them. Each man loudly claimed to be the choice of the lady Khandout. They all stood up when David entered. They gasped: "How can there be such a giant in this world?" David towered over these champions. He did not greet any of them.

"Welcome, David! Come join the feast."

They brought him a mattress. David sat down. They dipped their cups in a cauldron of forty-year-old wine and forty cups were offered to him at once, and some held out two cups for him.

David took a cup and smashed it to pieces against the wall. "Homewreckers, do you feed a camel with a spoon? This won't even wet my lips. What do you take me for, a sparrow?" He poured the wine back into the cauldron and raised the big copper to his lips. "To Khandout's health! Say, brothers, may it be sweet!"

They said: "May it be sweet."

David roared: "Godfather Gorgiz, food!"

Khandout sent in a hurry platters of pilav and roast meats, and servants brought clean bedding for David.

David crossed himself and turned to his table companions: "Hey, men, will somebody pray and bless this food before we eat it?"

They said: "David, today you are our honored guest. You eat first. We can eat later."

"Look here, brothers. If I eat first no food will be left for you. You will all starve."

"Do not worry, David. There is plenty of food for all. We are not hungry. We will eat later."

They were all pagans and did not know God. David drew their plates toward him and prayed:

"Our Father in heaven, hallowed be thy church, thy Kingdom come, thy name be done in heaven and on earth. Give us this day our almighty bread, and forgive us our transgresses, and lead us not into evil, but deliver us from temptation, for thine is the kingdom and the power and the glory forever amen. In the name of Jesus Christ, in the name of the God of God."

He cleaned up the food in all the plates, drank all the wine and brandy on the low brass table. Servants ran to Khandout Khatoun and said: "What is he? A man, pahlevan, or demon?" She said: "Today I saw my lord and master."

David was feeling good. "Pahlevans! If you pray to God as I do you will never go hungry. Your bellies will always be full, like mine."

They said: "David, we pray to our own god."

"You can pray to your false gods if you like but I will never allow a heathen to marry Khandout Khatoun. No man who does not acknowledge the one and only God can be her husband."

He asked them: "How long have you been here?"

One man said: "I have been here only a month, but many of us have been here for years."

"Well, doesn't Khandout Khatoun tell you whom she will marry?"

"Nobody knows her mind."

"And you sit here waiting?"

"What can we do?"

"Maybe she does not want to marry any of you, that is why she says nothing. Why don't you all go home?"

David got up from the table and staggered to the door. When he was gone the forty strongmen whispered among themselves: "We got him drunk. We will kill him when he gets back. Khandout Khatoun is not going to marry any of us with this turnip-eater from Sassoun sharing our food and drink. We are lost if we do not kill him."

They drew their swords from the scabbards hanging on the wall and hid them under the mattresses on which they sat. They looked very sad.

Gorgiz warned David: "Watch out, David, this is a death house, not a wedding hall."

He was blind drunk. He staggered back to his seat. His head dropped on his chest. He could not keep his eyes open. The forty strongmen reached for their swords under the mattresses and were going to strike him when "zing!" a hazel-nut struck the brass table. David raised his head, opened his eyes, looked around. They withdrew their hands, their hearts trembling with fear.

Soon David was nodding again, and "zing!" another hazel-nut struck the table, and the forty strongmen could not strike him. From her hall upstairs Khandout Khatoun could see what went on in the hall, and hear what her suitors said. She kept an anxious eye on David, and had a bag of nuts beside her to keep him awake.

"Gorgiz, open the gate! Gorgiz, open the gate! Gorgiz, open the gate!" Uncle Toros shouted.

Gorgiz was watering horses in the stable. He ran to the gate and said: "Welcome in God's name, Uncle Toros! Welcome in God's name, Uncle Toros! Welcome in God's name, Uncle Toros!" Three times.

Uncle Toros said: "Gorgiz, if you had not given God's name three times and opened the gate your head would have rolled into the Arax river."

When the ring he wore clouded on his finger Uncle Toros suspected David was in trouble. He flew to Tabriz on his six-footed Lagzi, and stormed into the hall just when David's head hit the floor and the pahlevans were reaching for their swords to strike him. What David got instead was a whipstroke, and jumped up, ready to tear the man who struck him to pieces — and grinned when he saw Uncle Toros standing before him with his whip.

"Uncle Toros, may God have mercy on you, you never whipped me before. It hurts."

"You fool! Did you think you came to Tabriz to play knuckle-bones with these men? Some day you will be killed by your own stupidity, you jackass."

"What happened? Why do you say that?"

Uncle Toros smirked. "Just take a look at all these swords under the mattresses and you will know what kind of game these pahlevans are playing."

He kicked the mattresses aside and David saw the sharp naked swords. He glanced at the wall: the scabbards were empty. "Are these your swords?" David asked their terrified owners. "Hand them over to me." Each man picked up his sword and handed it over shaking with fear. David broke their swords on his knee like so many matchsticks. They stampeded to the door and fled.

The gateman came in. David threw the broken twisted swords to him and said: "Godfather Gorgiz, take these to the stable and put them in my saddle-bags. They will make good horseshoes or a plowshare. The house is left to us, the yard to the chickens."

Outside, the strongmen said: "If we had struck David, he would have killed us all. It was a good thing the hazel-nuts kept him awake."

Uncle Toros said when they came out of the hall: "David, my soul, we chased them out, but have you seen the girl? Is she good, bad, what do you know about her? If she is a good girl we will ask for her hand."

Uncle Toros sent this message to Khandout's father: "We have to see the bride. My boy cannot marry her sight unseen. Arrange a meeting. Maybe my boy would not like her. Or she may not like him. These things are possible, and I do not want to have a bad marriage on my conscience. I am not a backwoodsman and I did not come here to sell whey cheese. Don't keep us waiting, if you want to save your city and your own neck."

When Khandout Khatoun heard about it she sent Gorgiz with this answer: "Don't be so impatient. You can see me tomorrow morning in the rose garden, when I take my Friday morning bath."

This meeting was arranged with her father's permission. David spruced up to look his best, and went to the rose garden with his uncle and Gorgiz. Uncle Toros crouched behind the trees by the gate to see what would happen. As the sun warmed up Khandout Khatoun entered the rose garden, with twenty maids walking in front of her, twenty maids behind her, carrying articles needed for her bath in silk parcels and baskets. David asked Gorgiz: "Which one is Khandout? They are all veiled." "She is the tallest. Taller than any of her forty maids by the length of two palms."

Khandout Khatoun took off her pretty garments, and plunged into the marble pool. After her bath she sat by the pool, and her maids helped her dress and prepare herself for the meeting with David. They combed and plaited her long hair. They polished her nails. They scented her body. Meanwhile the lady Khandout ate plums and pears and apples they picked for her in the royal orchard, and kept looking in her mirror.

No man could enter the rose garden. David was waiting outside. After she was ready to display her charms to him the lady rose to return ceremoniously to her hall, and again, twenty maids walked in front of her, twenty maids behind her. As the procession passed by where David stood, Gorgiz gave him the sign. Only the garden wall separated David from Khandout. He reached over the wall and grabbed her by her neck. The maids quickly withdrew. He pulled her toward him and lifted her veil. The minstrels did not tell him the half of it. He kissed her, not once, not twice, but a hundred times, and hungered for more. She said nothing. When he kissed her between her breasts, she slapped him. He fell against the wall with blood spurting out of his nose.

"Bread and wine, the living God!" David's hand reached for his mace. Uncle Toros jumped out from behind the trees and held his arm, did not let him strike her. "David, my boy, what are you doing?"

"God will give it to me or to her."

Khandout laughed and ran. David shouted after her: "Marry a man three hundred years old! I can wreck this city and leave it David's Ruin."

He turned to Uncle Toros. "What would you expect of a woman? Hair long, brains short."

Uncle Toros said: "The lion is a lion, male or female. Just think, David, what a child by you and Khandout would be like. You do not want to marry a teeny-weeny woman, do you?"

"Ah, Uncle Toros, our natures are alike. We are both quick-tempered. Teeny-weeny women do not interest me. I want a woman of proud spirit, strong, courageous. From the cow you get a calf, from the lion you get a cub. But I am not going to marry a girl who gives me a bloody nose and mouth for just kissing her."

David was so furious, and felt so disgraced, that he said to Gorgiz: "Godfather, bring my horse." Gorgiz brought him his horse. David mounted to go back to Sassoun. The gatekeeper ran to Khandout. "David is going back!" She sprang out of her hall and ran after David in her slippers. She took them off and ran in her silk socks. She took them off and ran barefoot, crying: "David, don't go! Don't go! Don't go!" He kept going, but not too fast. She cut her feet on the rocks. A sharp thorn pierced her toes. She was not used to running barefoot. Her feet bled. "David, come back! See the condition I am in, and then go. Pity me, if you love the Cross, do not have me on your conscience."

When David heard her say, "If you love the Cross," he turned back. She stood in a pool of blood, waiting for him. She said: "David, I will run after you as long as there is any breath left in me. Why are you so angry with me?"

"I came for you all the way from Sassoun, and got a bloody nose."

She took him back to the rose garden, washed his bloody face at the marble fountain. She picked white and red roses with her own white hands and held them under his nose.

She said: "Did you see those forty men? Many of them have been here three, five, seven years, and not a single one of them has seen me yet. You came, and you did not even greet me. Before we could sit down and have a talk, before we could find out whether we like each other's conversation and get acquainted, you grabbed me and kissed me.

"David, my father gave permission for only two kisses. When you kissed me on my forehead, I said to myself, it's lawful, he came a long way to see me. When you kissed me on my cheeks, I thought, well, he is young and ardent. When you kissed my neck I said nothing, for Uncle Toros' sake. When you kissed my shoulders, I still said nothing, for God's sake. But how dare you kiss me between my breasts? That's unlawful."

"And it's unlawful of me to live as a man if a woman can punch me in the nose."

"When we marry, you can kiss me as often as you like. David, you are making me an Armenian woman even before we are married. If you are the warrior son of Lion-Meherr, I am the warrior daughter of kings."

Her words softened his heart. She seized him by the hand and led him to her hall.

The next morning Uncle Toros went to her father and asked for her hand. The Emir[2] said: "How many heads has he brought me that he expects to marry my daughter? Khandout is betrothed to Shapouh, Shah of Iran. If David can go against him and kill him, he can have my daughter. If Shapouh wins, then she is promised to him already."

Uncle Toros told David what the Emir said. David said: "Good. You go back to Sassoun, I will go to Teheran."

That evening, as David was entertained again by Khandout Khatoun, she poured water over his hands, rubbed his neck, spoke many endearing words to him. She was very loving as they drank the forty-year-old pomegranate wine.

He said: "If I do not return with Shapouh's head in seven days then you know I am dead. Don't leave my body to the dogs and vultures. Bury me with a requiem mass, by the Christian rite, with priests and vardapets. You can recognize my body by this cross embedded in my flesh, on my right arm."

She kissed the Victory Cross and said: "David, my father, my mother, my brothers, all are pagans, but I am Christian. I was so glad to hear you say Our Father in the hall. I hope to God no king, no pahlevan, can defeat you."

They spent hours together. The next morning David went to the stable to get his horse. She ran after him, crying: "David, David, wait, I will go to the stable myself and bring you your horse." She hurried to the stable and found the horses of the forty strongmen huddled fearfully together in a corner of the building, and David's horse standing like a mountain among them. The horse did not recognize her when she tried to lead him out and shook his head. Khandout hit the floor. "David, your horse will kill me!" He rushed in, took her in his arms, raised her to her feet. He said to his horse: "May God have mercy on you, can't you see she is a woman? Does a man strike a woman?" To Khandout he said: "Don't be afraid to touch him. You can lead him out now. He took you for a stranger." She led him out, threw the saddle on him, and David tightened the girth. He mounted and galloped off.

"By God, Iran, I am coming!"

On reaching Teheran he stopped before the Shah's palace and yelled: "Shapouh, come out." The Shah stepped out and saw a huge horseman who would not dismount, waiting for him before his palace.

David said: "Hey, Shapouh, are you the betrothed of Khandout Khatoun? I came to fight you in single combat, and God will give it to me or to you. The lady Khandout belongs to the victor."

The Shah howled like a wolf when he heard him mention the name of Khandout Khatoun. He ordered his horse to be brought to him, issued commands to his troops. They rode out to the arena and began fighting while the troops stood by. David clubbed him with his mace and knocked him off his horse. He jumped on him and cut off his head. The Shah's troops did not dare make a move as David threw the king's head into his saddlebag and flew back to Tabriz.

The Emir could not believe it until Shapouh's head was shown to him. When David was summoned to the divan, the Emir and his ministers exchanged glances of wonder and admiration. They had never seen such a warrior before. The Emir was glad to have the Shah's head, but he had other enemies: Oghan, Toghan, the chain-breakers; the King of Khurasan; the Black King; Lorva Hamza. They all wanted his daughter. The mounted troops of his enemies were moving on Tabriz, and he received a new message from Pahlevan Hamza: "I must have Khandout Khatoun without delay. Dress her, veil her, send her to me as my bride."

The Emir summoned his ministers to council in his divan.

He asked his vizier: "What troops are these? I am told they are so many a man who sees them drops his handkerchief from sheer fright."

The vizier said: "What troops are they? They are all coming against us because of your impossible daughter. She brought forty pahlevans here and does not like any of them. She brought Gorgiz here, and made him her gatekeeper. She brought David of Sassoun here, and bloodied his nose in the rose garden. Maybe she knows what she is doing, what she wants. But this is her fight, not ours. We cannot raise another army to defend our city just because she cannot make up her mind."

"Then I would have to dress her, veil her, send her to Hamza."

The Emir went to have a talk with his daughter. She said: "I would rather be dead than marry Hamza, or Oghan, Toghan, the King of Khurasan, the Black King, the King of Chin-ma-Chin, and all the others. If they are so brave and powerful let them come and take me away by force. Let them try and see what happens! David is here."

What did she do next? She wanted to test her forty suitors and sent Gorgiz to them with this message: "I will marry the man who fights for me."

All forty said: "Why should we fight for her? Let the man who was hit by her apple and is kissing her, drinking with her, fight for her. This is David's war, not ours."

Gorgiz repeated to Khandout Khatoun what her suitors said.

"Very well then, it is my fight," David said. "I am going."

"I will go with you," she said.

"No, you are a woman, you stay here. I have been praying to God for a chance like this. This is the answer to my prayers. But I do not want these forty pahlevans to be feasting in the hall while I am gone. They have no right to stay here if they will not fight for you."

She went down to the hall, locked the door, and tossed them out of the window one by one. She could have killed them. They fled with broken necks, arms, legs. She said: "Did you think I would leave David and marry one of you?" When David came down to the hall and saw it empty he roared with laughter. "Thank God, my woman is braver than I am."

David spent another day with her. Next morning David had a mass sung for him and took the communion. As he saddled his horse and mounted, Khandout became panicky. She loved him. She was afraid he would not come back alive this time, and after seven days she would have to put on her fighting clothes and go find his body among the slain.

She cried: "Gorgiz, close the gate, don't let David go!"

Gorgiz closed the gate. David leaped over the wall and was gone.

God knows how far he went when he saw a horseman speeding toward him through whirling clouds of dust. When the other rider came closer David recognized him as St. Sargis. All the Daredevils belonged to St. Sargis' brood, he was their chief and commander, and David wanted to kiss him. St. Sargis said: "Let me first kiss the Holy Emblem on you." David took out his Holy Emblem, the cross of Marouta's High Mother of God, and St. Sargis kissed it, after which David kissed St. Sargis. St. Sargis said: "You can go now, and may God be with you."

David rode on, and met another horseman through clouds of dust. Uncle Ohan, riding his Black stallion, thundered at him:

"You son-of-a-bitch! You have no more brains than the calf of a buffalo. Don't we have enough girls in Sassoun that you come all the way to Iran to find a wife? Do you think you are going to fight Kouz-Badin, or Misra Melik? The Emir of India, the Caliph of Baghdad? It is not your big brother this time, but pahlevan Hamza! And Oghan, Toghan, the chain-breakers. And the King of Khurasan. The Black King. Demons all. Why, the ring Hamza wears on his little finger is thicker than your arm."

David said: "Uncle Ohan, it can't be helped. I have to go against them. God will give it to me or to them."

"They will chew you up. Turn back."

"Goodbye. I am going."

"Wait! I will go with you."

They rode on together. What brought Uncle Ohan to his aid was another bad dream he had about David. He dreamt David's feet were caught in a large jar of pitch and he could not extricate himself. Later in the night he dreamt again David was tied with iron chains to iron poles. He shook his wife and said: "Light the lamp and lead my Black horse out of the stable. I have to go find David. He is in a very tight spot." Sara said: "Go to sleep, old man. David is enjoying himself in Khandout's bosom. What does he care about you?" She refused to get up. He sprang out of bed. "Are you mad, old man? Or do you lust for her white flesh yourself? If you go after David I will have the executioner chop off your head." He struck her, and broke a rib. He led out his Black horse, mounted, and reached David in the twinkling of an eye.

Flying across the plains of Iran they came to the tents of the Black King, and Oghan, Toghan, the chain-breakers. These tents were beyond counting, like trees in a forest. "Bread and wine, the living God, Marouta's High Mother of God, the Victory Cross on my right arm!" they shouted and attacked the mounted troops with drawn swords. They chopped them down in rows. They were like a couple of hungry wolves rampaging through flocks of spring lambs, sinking their fangs into their throats, throwing them left and right as they leaped this way and that way on their horses, and the ground ran with blood. After six days of furious fighting only two men survived the slaughter: Oghan, Toghan, the chain-breakers.

"You go after Oghan, I will go after Toghan," David said, as Oghan fled east, Toghan west.

They captured both of them. "They will make nice presents for the lady Khandout," David said. "She can use two more servants."

"Don't kill us," the two begged him. "We shall gladly light your pipe, prepare your coffee, tea, serve you faithfully to the end of our lives."

"Hold them," David said to his uncle. "I will go get Hamza and meet you here."

Ohan began to pray, as David raced on to Hamza's city.

The dreaded pahlevan sat on his throne in his mansion, and the King of Khurasan was with him. David saluted as he entered. The King of Khurasan stared at him from under his brows, which hung over his chest and were tied behind his back with a dagger. Hamza's lower lip reached the floor.

"Who are you?" Hamza said.

"David."

"What do you want?"

"I came to ask you to give me a keepsake for Khandout Khatoun, something she would like to have from you as your betrothed."

Hamza took the ring off his little finger and threw it to David. "Take this to her."

David took the ring, passed his arm through it, up to his neck. Then he took it off and threw it back to Hamza. "I did not come here for your ring. This is not worth taking to her. This is nothing."

"Then what do you want me to give you for Khandout Khatoun?"

"Your head, Hamza, I want your head."

The hideous champion, terror of the world, screamed at him: "Are you one of Mad Sergo's³ brood?"

"I am," David said, and crossed himself.

Hamza sprang from his throne and advanced toward David, his lower lip sweeping the floor. David grappled with him, and with the King of Khurasan. They fought for hours. "Jesus Christ, help me," David said. He brought Hamza down with a savage throw, he brought the King of Khurasan down with another throw, jumped on them, struck off their heads. He drove his sword into their skulls, swung them over to his shoulder, walked to his horse, and put them in his saddlebags. On his way back to his uncle he saw that Hamza's tongue, sharp like a plowshare, cut a furrow across the plain.

Uncle Ohan was waiting for David with Oghan, Toghan.

David said: "Uncle Ohan, I will go down to the river, clean up and change my clothes."

When he returned he saw that his uncle had cut off the heads of both captives.

"Why did you do it, Uncle Ohan? We do not kill prisoners of war. Their hands were tied. They were just about dead. Do you murder the dead?"

"They rolled their eyes to scare me. They cursed you. They tried to kill me. Son, you can't leave these heathen kings alive. You have to finish them off."

They argued, came to blows. Ohan struck hard at David, and would have killed him if he could. David threw him down. Ohan fell half dead.

"Hey, son, you don't mean to kill me?"

David gave him his hand and helped him get to his feet. They kissed each other on the head and made up. They threw the heads of Oghan, Toghan also into their saddlebags and set out for Khandout's city, riding across the battlefield where the dead lay in heaps.

On their way back they saw a black horseman mixing sky and earth together as he came flying toward them. This warrior shouted to David: "Take care, I am not the King of Khurasan or the pahlevan Hamza." And cast off his mace. David was under the belly of his horse. The mace struck the stirrup, fell to the ground. David was up in the saddle again.

"Yeah, bread and wine, the living God!" He was going to strike him on the head when the horseman wheeled around and fled. His helmet fell off. David saw the long hair behind her back, and recognized her as the lady Khandout, whom he had left in Tabriz more than seven days ago. He did not let her know, and struck a boulder instead, tearing off a rock that forty pairs of buffaloes could not move. Uncle Ohan was hurt badly during his scuffle with David and was resting behind the trees during this fight.

"Hey, what are you doing here? Trying to find your man's carcass? I killed him. He has been dead three days. I have his head in my saddlebag. If you need a husband, I can be your husband," David said.

She turned around and looked suspiciously at his horse, but did not recognize David in the dusk, as he had changed his clothes and covered his face.

Khandout said: "A hundred men like you are not worth his little finger. It is not the likes of you that can kill my man. But if you killed him, I will kill you! You will die like a dog. If you are so brave, fight me on foot."

They jumped off their horses and he pretended to be wrestling with her. He grabbed her by her waist and pinned her down on her back.

"See, this is what you get for giving me a bloody nose."

"David!"

"Are you blind? Can't you see me?" He helped her to her feet. "You were going to disgrace me twice. Well, I took care of your enemies. Are you satisfied?"

"I am satisfied," she said, as he embraced her and kissed her.

Uncle Ohan came over, all smiles, and David presented his uncle. "He is a great man," he said. David winked and she kissed Ohan's hand. She had brought healing salves with her and applied them to his wound.

They rode back together. She said on their way:

"A few years ago the King of the West wanted me for his son, and they gave me to him. I was waiting for my husband in the bedroom. My husband came in and stood by the bed. He said, 'What is this? I have heard a man goes to bed first.' I said, 'Man, come, come, lie beside me.' He was silent. He did not say he would, he did not say he would not. I seized him by the hand to pull him to bed. His arm came off. I thought, well, he is the son of a king, he does not have to plow or sow in the fields like a farmer's son, he might do as a husband even with one arm missing. I took hold of his other arm, and it came off too. I thought, he is the son of a king, I will be satisfied even if both arms are missing. A little later, I shook him by the leg and his leg came off. I was so surprised! He gasped out his last breath and fell dead by the bedside. It was then I realized my own strength. The King of the West said: 'This bride is a killer, send her back to her parents.' When I came home I made a vow: I will not marry another man, unless he can pin me down on my back. And that's what you did today. God gave me to you, and gave you to me. I am your woman, you are my man. I will go with you anywhere."

They rode into Khandout's city side by side, with Uncle Ohan leading on his Black horse. They dismounted before the garden-palace, washed up, changed their bloody clothes. They ate a hearty dinner, after which Uncle Ohan mounted his horse and flew back to Sassoun, and David and Khandout went to bed ...

The Emir was delighted to have also the heads of pahlevan Hamza and of Oghan, Toghan, the chain-breakers, placed before him. He rounded up all the vardapets, priests and deacons in the city for David's wedding in a church, and bagpipes and drums played for seven days and nights. The strongmen Khandout tossed out of the hall came to congratulate David. They all became Christians and entered his service.

NOTES

[1] Chimishkik Sultana of Akhlat: This warlike queen is probably a symbol of the Roman power in Armenia and in at least one variant, DS, vol. I, p. 1014, she is identified with "Pope Frank," who of course is a symbol of the West, the King of Franks. "Pope Frank, named Chimishkik Sultana," is the way this reciter presents her. And in at least another variant Chimishkik Sultana is a man who himself is in love with Khandout Khatoun. In Armenian, it is Sultan, not Sultana, and this title may be applied to both men and women. In DS, vol. III, p. 511, she is said to be a Turkish lady. In the 12th century Akhlat became the capital of Moslem rulers of this part

of Armenia, Shahi Armen, and Egyptians took it in 1207, thus surrounding Sassoun from all sides. Roman, Arab, or Turkish, or ruled by a demon, White Dev, Akhlat is a hostile city. Armenian and Roman, or Byzantine Greek, were often at war. The enemy was not always a Moslem.

The name Chimishkik Sultan reminds us of John Tsimsces of the Byzantine Empire, Tsimisc being the Greek spelling of Chimishk in Anglicized form. There are some interesting historical parallels. See *David of Sassoun* (collection of essays in Armenian) USSR Academy of Sciences — Armenian Section, Erevan, 1939, p. 39. One of several Armenian-born emperors of the later Roman Empire, John Tsimisces comes from this same region in Armenia. Gibbon on John Tsimisces:

"A noble and valiant Armenian . . . The stature of John Zimisces was below the ordinary standard; but this diminutive body was endowed with strength, beauty, and the soul of a hero . . . the guilt of Zimisces was forgotten in the splendour of his virtues . . . his gentle and generous behavior delighted all who approached his person . . . his personal valour and activity were signalized on the Danube and the Tigris, the ancient boundaries of the Roman world; and by his double triumph over the Russians and Saracens he deserved the twin titles of saviour of the empire and conqueror of the East." (*The Decline and Fall of the Roman Empire*, vol. 2, pp. 899-900, Modern Library edition.)

[2] Emir of Tabriz: In the first variant, Gurbo's, Khandout's father is Emir of Kagizman (DS, vol. II, p. 30). Kagizman is a small city to the southwest of Erevan, now on the Turkish side of the border, but a medieval ruler of that city need not of course be an Armenian. The references to Khandout's Iranian origin are too numerous to mention. "There was a Persian lady, Khandout Hanum . . .," DS, vol. I, p. 517; "David plowed until noon, mounted his horse, reached Tabriz in the evening," DS, vol. I, p. 362. It is repeatedly stated that her family is pagan, that is to say, Moslem. She is even presented as a daughter of Oghan, Toghan, dreadful enemies of Sassoun. These names Oghan, Toghan, are always coupled together, and in some variants Oghan, Toghan is one person. Emir means commander in Arabic, and Khandout's father is an independent chieftain, a prince of high rank in Iranian Azerbaijan. The Armenian bards present this Iranian princess as a perfection of all feminine virtues, even though she belongs to an enemy race. In some variants she resides in Blue Rock, and her nationality is not given. Her father is variously referred to as an Emir, a King, a Prince or Lord. Khandout may mean "Khan's-daughter" in Persian.

[3] Mad Sergo: Sergo is folksy variant of Sargis, and St. Sargis is Armenia's most popular saint next to St. Karapet, the Herald of Christ.

DAVID'S DEATH

Nine months, nine days, nine hours passed and the divinity blessed David with a son. Now you don't get a little sickly child from David and Khandout Khatoun, but when they bathed the baby they saw that one of his hands was tightly closed. They tried everything, but could not open his hand. They called David. He came and rubbed it with his fingers until the hand opened. A drop of blood gleamed in the boy's palm.

David laughed. The Emir asked him: "Why do you laugh?" David said: "My boy will hold the world in the palm of his hand, like a drop of blood. He will shed ten times more blood than I have done, he will be ten times more ruthless with the the heathen."

The Emir said: "David, let us not have any more bloodshed. You are too bloodthirsty."

The boy seemed to have squeezed that drop of blood out of his mother's liver. They christened him Meherr, after David's father. One day David entered the room where the baby was sleeping and did not see the gauze on his face rising and falling. He thought the child was not the fruit of his loins. He said to the lady Khandout: "When I was still in the cradle the gauze on my face blew up to the ceiling. Why is this baby so weak?"

The lady Khandout said: "Wait until the forty-days are over, and then come and look at him."

When the forty-days were over and David entered the baby's room he saw not only the gauze but the cloth covering on the cradle flying up to the ceiling with every breath Meherr took.

He grew by the day, by the hour, and not like other children by the year, or by the month.

For a year, living quietly at home, David did not know what was going on in the world. He led a peaceful life until the new Shah of Iran sent a letter to Pope Frank, in which he said: "A man from Sassoun came to my country and destroyed my army. They call him David. There was a most beautiful lady in Iran, Khandout Khatoun by name, whom he took away by force and married."

Pope Frank did not believe the Shah. He asked his vizier: "Read this letter and see if it makes sense. How can one man destroy an entire army of a hundred thousand?" The vizier read the letter, and laughed.

"Your majesty, this is a lie, impossible."

They wrote to David: "We hear you are a very strong man. Come to fight us if you can."

The letter was delivered to David, but he could not read in that language. He showed it to his wife. "Khandout, what does it say in this paper?" She read it and asked him: "Who brought it?" He said: "Two men." She said: "Take them to the hall." David fed them and treated them well, and had them stay overnight. The next morning Khandout answered Pope Frank's letter:

"We do not know you, we never heard your name. What do you want from us? Why threaten war? But don't come alone if you must fight David. Bring another king with you. You would need his help."

She folded the letter, put it in a packet, and said: "David, take this to the two men in the hall. Give them clothes of honor to wear, ten gold pieces, and two fine horses, and let them go back to their country."

Khandout Khatoun told him nothing about the answer she wrote to Pope Frank. When the King received her letter he called his vizier and other ministers to council, and they were amazed when they read it. They said: "He slaughtered the Shah's troops, and now he tells us, make it two kings. We will ask the King of Chin-ma-Chin to join us." The vizier objected: "Need we call the King of Chin-ma-Chin to our aid when we have only one man against us?"

The King gathered his troops and sent another letter to David: "I am coming. Meet me in the plain of Moush." Messengers came to Tabriz and handed the King's letter to David. David gave it to Khandout to read it for him. She said: "I answered his first letter and said bring another king with you if you want to fight David, to scare him off. But now he is coming alone and expects you to fight him in the plain of Moush."

David said: "Why didn't you tell me before? I would not have let him come as far as the plain of Moush."

"I did not think he would. If you wish, I will go with you."

"Do you think there would be enough men for both of us? Can't I kill all of them myself?"

David put on his fighting clothes. "Don't come after me. You are not my wife if you do. We have nothing to fear. God is merciful."

He mounted, bid his wife farewell, and rode out to Moush. The plain was covered with tents more numerous than the stars in heaven, and more troops were arriving. He had not done any fighting for a year. He cried: "Yeah, Marouta's High Mother of God, the Victory Cross on my right arm!" And struck. The commanders asked their king to send more reinforcements. The king was surprised by what happened and said: "Come back, don't fight any more." A torrent of blood carried off the dead, and the rest fled in disorder. David cried after them: "Don't run away, I will not kill you. Just show me where your king is." They said: "Go to our city and you will find him there."

David spurred his horse and rode out to the city of Pope Frank. He dispatched to him this message: "Come to see me." The king came, saw David on his horse, and fled. David caught him, struck him, killed him. He appointed a new king in his place. He killed the great men, the princes, and put the little men in their places. He said: "Never fight again, no more war as long as you live." He established good order in the city and said before his departure: "Write to me if you need me, and I will come back." They were in such awe of him that they said: "David, we shall obey you and serve you until death."

Uncle Toros wrote from Sassoun: "David, the throne of Sassoun is empty, we feel like orphans. Come back."

Two stout-hearted messengers brought the letter to David. When David read it he said: "Uncle Toros is right. I have to go back." To Khandout he said: "Get ready, we are leaving for Sassoun tomorrow morning."

The Emir said: "David, I gave you my daughter with the understanding you would stay with us. Eat, drink, enjoy life. My home is your home. Don't take my daughter away from me. I have other, powerful enemies and if you leave, they will attack and destroy my city."

"No, I have to go," David said. "I have stayed here long enough. They need me in Sassoun. I have my own city to defend."

The Emir said: "Then let me keep Little Meherr with me, until he grows older. Your son is my son. David, if I had a son like yours my enemies would never dare attack me. He would defend me like a fort."

The infant stayed with his grandfather in Tabriz, and David and Khandout Khatoun packed their belongings and loaded them on a hundred horses. She received a large dowry and many costly gifts. They mounted and rode out of Tabriz side by side.

The Emir wanted to keep Little Meherr as his adopted son,

to make him forget his real father and his people. He thought he could use Meherr not only against his remaining enemies, but against Sassoun itself if need be. He gave secret orders to his men to kill David and bring his daughter back.

David was attacked in a narrow valley filled with the Emir's warriors. Khandout suspected her father's plot and she had David put on his armor and she herself wore her armor and fought beside him. She killed five thousand men and saved David's life.

When they reached Akhlat they found a barricade of carts and logs thrown across the road. The people of that city were up in arms and unwilling to let them pass. They said: "David came to our city and made love to our queen, and then he married another woman. We are offended by his conduct. We will not let him pass through our city unchallenged."

Presently the Sultana of Akhlat came up on her fiery horse and said: "So it is you, David. You vowed to marry me, we exchanged rings. You left me with child and married Khandout Khatoun. Why, am I not pretty enough to be your wife? If you are such a great hero, I challenge you to fight me in single combat. Either I kill you, and both Khandout and I are left widows, or you kill me. But you have to kill me before I let you sleep in her bosom."

"I cannot fight a woman in single combat. Have ten thousand horseman with you if you expect me to fight with you."

"I do not need ten thousand horsemen. I can fight as well as any man."

David said: "Chimishkik Sultana, let me take my wife home and I promise to come back in seven days and fight."

She said: "I cannot trust your word. Put your hand on your Holy Emblem and swear on Marouta's High Mother of God and the Victory Cross on your right arm that you will come back in seven days."

David said in his mind: "Fight this old bitch? Single combat with a woman is not to my taste. I have found the true companion of my heart, but this sorceress wants me to swear an oath." He put his hand on his breast and said: "I swear by Marouta's High Mother of God and the Victory Cross on my right arm that I will come back in seven days."

She said, brandishing her sword: "I will be waiting for you!"

David took his wife home, and seven groups of minstrels played for seven days and nights. Everybody, the young and old, welcomed David back to Sassoun with his beautiful warrior wife. Everybody was happy, except Sara. Sara's heart was torn with envy when she saw Khandout Khatoun. She thought: "David will never marry me now or make love to me." She was sick over it, and stayed in bed.

Sleeping in Khandout's bosom, in his own home, David forgot his oath.

Back in his native Sassoun, David thought of the forty pahlevans in Tabriz. "They are on my conscience," he said. "I took Khandout away from them. I have heard there are many beautiful girls in Georgia. I will go find them and take them to Georgia with me."

Well, he was David, and he was gone again. He rode to forty countries and found the forty strongmen, and they were off to Georgia together. An old man they met on the road told them the girls of Azerbaijan are just as beautiful. David found a wife for each, in Georgia, in Azerbaijan, each marrying the girl of his choice. They said: "We thank you, David, for making us happy. We have now attained our wish." He picked the daughter of the King of Georgia to take her home with him as a maid for his wife, put her on his horse, and set out for Sassoun. This girl was the most beautiful of all. The King of Chin-ma-Chin wanted her for his own son. The King of Chin-ma-Chin was told by his men: "A man from Sassoun kidnapped your bride." The King of Chin-ma-Chin said: "God will give it to me or to you," and pursued him with his army, but could not catch up with David.

What happened in Sassoun meanwhile? The lady Khandout went back to her parents and lived with them until Uncle Toros brought her back to Sassoun accompanied by Little Meherr. When scarcely a year old Meherr rose up and wandered through the streets of Tabriz, pulled down poplar trees and killed scores of young boys as they played see-saw. When he struck his ball, boys fell dead in rows. In Sassoun he continued his mischiefs. He built a bridge over the river, then he stood on the bridge and would not let anybody pass. "Turn back," he would say. "Do you think I built this bridge for you?" And when they did not use his bridge he beat them and said: "Why don't you use my bridge?" Princely men complained to Uncle Toros and Uncle Ohan, and they admonished the boy, but he was too wild to listen to their advice.

Meherr grew up to be seven, and still no sign of David. He asked his mother: "Where is my father? Don't I have a father? Children call me an orphan, a bastard. They say, 'What are you so proud about when you have no father?'"

She said: "My boy, your father is David. He went to Georgia, and has not returned yet."

"Mother, I will go find my father and bring him back. He is alone. He may need me."

She showed him the way to Georgia. Meherr mounted his horse and went to find his father. He saw a dark-bearded man coming down a mountain-road with a girl on the back of his horse.

"Good day to you, papik," he greeted the old man.

"God's day."

"Who is the pretty girl with you? Where are you taking her?"

"Where I take her is my own affair."

"Give her to me."

"What would a young boy like you do with a woman?"

"Give her to me. Aren't you ashamed? An old man with a beard, with such a young girl. It's not right."

"Right for you, not right for me."

"I am young and unmarried."

David tried to push the insolent youth out of his way. Meherr stopped him and wanted the girl. "I will take her away from you."

David never knew what fear was, but this boy scared him. He said:

"I have crossed many a river and sea
And the flies on my horse never got wet;
A braver man than I I never met
And here I run into a little stream
That does not rise to the shanks of my horse
And I am afraid. What happened to me?
I have flown across icy peaks sky-high
Leaped over many a gorge and rocky vale
And no man has been more daring than I
In a brawl or raid I was never afraid
And now by this stream I halt and turn pale."

Meherr asked: "Am I the little stream? Get off your horse. I will wrestle you."

David dismounted and said: "Wait, I will take the girl to a safe spot before we fight." He took her to the top of a hill, and came back. They crashed against each other like a couple of mountains. The sky darkened with dust. The sweat and blood pouring from their bodies muddied the ground under their feet. David tried to save his soul from the fury of the gigantic boy who pounded him down to his knees, broke his ribs, broke his back, and then drew his sword to cut off his head. He was amazed by what happened. He met more than his match in this young boy.

"Hey, whose son are you?"

"I am the son of David of Sassoun."

"I am David of Sassoun."

The boy wept and kissed his hands. "Forgive me, father, for sinning against you."

David embraced his son. They smiled delightedly at each other. They took the Georgian girl and rode back to Sassoun together. She was betrothed to Meherr, and they sat down to eat, drink, and make merry at a feast.

The Emir of Tabriz said to his five sons: "I hear David is back after conquering more kingdoms. When a man loses a chicken, he goes after it. Go visit your sister in Sassoun. I worry about her. How is she? Come back and tell me."

The visit of her five brothers pleased Khandout very much. She made a big fuss over them. She kept them for two weeks, would not let them go back. The Emir's sons went hunting every morning, and took Meherr with them. Meherr was the only one who rode back from Dzovasar empty-handed. He was a bold fearless boy, light on his feet, a good shot with the bow, and his parents were puzzled. David said: "I cannot understand. Are you my son? Or are you no better than boys in the streets? Can't you even shoot a little bird with your bow? Your uncles come back every day loaded with wild sheep. When I was your age I shot wild bulls."

Meherr laughed: "Pap, I kill them; they bring them."

"Bring them yourself."

"I will bring you a few wild sheep tomorrow."

The next day Meherr shot several wild sheep and boars, hung them from his saddle, and started for home. His five uncles rode after him. "Meherr, wait, shoot a few more."

"This is enough for me. I am taking them to my pap."

"We will carry them for you."

"I can carry them myself."

"We will give you knucklebones."

"No. From now on you do your own hunting."

They jumped off their horses and tried to take the wild sheep and boars away from him. Meherr also dismounted. There was a fight. Meherr lifted them and brought them down one by one, driving all five into the ground up to their waists. Then he rode home.

David was sleeping. Khandout woke him and said: "See how many wild sheep Meherr brought you."

David opened his eyes, looked at all the game Meherr placed before him, smiled with approval. Khandout said: "Meherr, where are your uncles? Why didn't they come home with you?"

"I don't know. I left them standing in the road, grinning."

David slapped his knees. "My God, he killed them."

He ran out to see what happened to his five guests. He had matched his strength against his son's and knew how deadly Meherr could be. He found all five of them dead, their mouths open, their white teeth shining. He came home and told his wife. She could not believe it.

"Why did you kill them?" David asked.

"Because they cheated me. They always bragged about the wild sheep I shot."

David slapped him, and the boy did not seem to feel it. He slapped him again, and said: "If I had struck an iron pole with this hand of mine I would have broken it in two." Meherr sat there saying nothing. David's hand crashed against the boy's face for the third time. Meherr grabbed him by the waist, raised him a foot from the floor. His mother prayed:

> "Blessed is merciful God
> Great is thy mercy, Lord
> Help, help! Break up this fight
> Between father and son
> Before it is too late
> And they kill each other.
> Blessed is merciful God
> Great is thy mercy, Lord
> Help, help! Break up this fight
> Between father and son
> Before it is too late

And they kill each other.
Blessed is merciful God
Great is thy mercy, Lord
Help, help! Break up this fight
Between father and son
Before it is too late
And they kill each other."

God's angel came down from heaven and stood between David and his son.

Meherr said, holding David by the waist: "You had a right to slap me once, as my father, and I said nothing. The second time I said nothing for God's sake. You struck me for the third time. You can't hurt me, but I can hurt you. A slap by you is like the breezes of Dzovasar. It just ruffles my hair. If I dropped you now you would dry up in the ground like them."

He put him down unharmed. David dreaded the power of his son. He cursed him: "Your seed would devour the world. O sweet God, make him heirless and deathless upon this earth until Christ comes back on judgment day."

In those days God heard a father's curse, and David was a just man. The angel Gabriel drew the manly vein out of Meherr's loins so that he would never have a child of his own.

"Get out of my sight, I don't want to see you again," David said.

Meherr angrily walked out of the house. Khandout went out to look for him, but he had gone, disappeared, with the Georgian girl. Khandout's five brothers were buried with a requiem mass, in the presence of princes and vardapets. David paid for the funeral expenses. It cost him plenty of gold pieces.

David said to Khandout: "My side hurts. Heat a copperful of water and give me a bath." His right arm hurt also, but he said nothing about it.

She heated the water and brought it to him. When he took off his clothes, she began to cry.

"Wife, why are you crying?"

"David, the Victory Cross on your right arm has turned black."

"I wish you had not seen it. Don't throw it in my face."

They called a physician and applied healing salves to the festering wound on his arm, but it grew worse, it was eating into his flesh. He said: "There is no cure for this pain. It was not my son who struck me on my way back to Sassoun, but this cross. I forgot my oath. I would have to go and fight Chimishkik Sultana. I will tear that whore to pieces."

He sent her word he would be in Akhlat. David was not his old self. People noticed his growing weakness. Uncle Toros said: "May I go blind, David, did you swear an oath on your Holy Emblem?"

"I had to, to get rid of Chimishkik Sultana. She wouldn't let us pass through her city unless I swore on my Holy Emblem I would be back to fight her in single combat. And now I am a sick man. Yes, Uncle Toros, I lost my strength. She may kill me. This may be my last fight. But I have to go clear my conscience."

Everybody was in tears. They all wanted to go to Akhlat with David, they wanted to fight for him. He said: "I must go and fight her alone." They tried to prevent him from going. He said: "Two lies are worse than one."

In those days men did not break an oath. David mounted his horse and rode out to Akhlat unarmed. He halted before the queen's castle. She spoke to him from her window: "David, I have been waiting for you. You promised to be back in seven days. It has been seven years. You swore on your Holy Emblem. I will meet you in the arena in about an hour. I have to dress up."

He said: "While you are getting ready I will go bathe in the river and wash my horse."

A great officer of her court told the queen: "Daredevils of

Sassoun are a waterborn, fiery race. They lose their strength and dry up if they can't get to water."

She said in her mind: "I have a strong army with me, but I know I cannot kill David in the arena. I have to kill him while he is sleeping, or bathing in the river."

David's horse would not cross the bridge. Jalali sensed the danger. Under the bridge the queen's seven-year-old daughter was hiding behind the reeds and rushes with a bow in her hand, and arrows smeared with deadly poison in her quiver. David spurred his horse into the stream, which was not very deep, and the horse got stuck in the mud. When they reached the other side David was covered with mud. He dismounted, took off his clothes to clean them. An arrow struck him in the back and tore his guts out. He bellowed like forty buffaloes in agony. Uncle Ohan heard him in Sassoun. He said: "Boys, that was David. They struck him."

Ohan wrapped himself in his seven buffalo-hides, drew the plow-chain around his chest and yelled: "David, we are coming!"

Uncle Ohan, Uncle Toros, Colicky Vergo, and other kinsmen of David's, with a hundred warriors, jumped on their horses and rode out to Akhlat. They reached the river and found David sprawled in a pool of blood, moaning in pain. His horse stood beside him and would not let a stranger get close.

Uncle Toros asked him: "Boy, who struck you?"

"I don't know who struck me," David answered. "It came from under the bridge, behind those reeds. Pull out the arrow. I am dying."

They pulled it out.

They searched through the reeds and caught a young girl with blue eyes, dead under the bridge, still holding her bow. She died of fright, when David bellowed like that. When they brought her to David he said: "My own daughter, my own seed killed me." These were David's last words.

Uncle Toros said: "With David dead, the heathen will come to gouge out our eyes and eat our bread."

Uncle Ohan said: "We are a kingdom without a king. What shall we do now?"

Uncle Toros said: "Call Meherr. He will hear you wherever he is."

Ohan put on his buffalo-hides and called in his thunderous voice:

"David's son Meherr, hearken to my voice
Stop drinking the red pomegranate wine
The light of Sassoun is burning no more
And the heartless foes will be at our door
Your father is dead, come avenge his death
So that once again our great star will shine."

Meherr heard him in Azerbaijan, where he was making merry with forty drinking companions. He put down his wine cup and said:

"I heard a voice from east or west
From north or south I do not know
I think I heard my uncle's voice
Calling me home and I must go."

He mounted his horse and flew to Akhlat. He asked: "Who killed my father?" His blood boiled.

"The heathen killed him," his uncles said. "We are surrounded by enemies from all sides."

Right then and there Meherr made a vow: "Bread and wine, the living God, I will destroy this city and cut up the roots of the heathen."

This was Meherr's first oath. He fell on his knees and wept bitterly before his father's corpse. They could not pull him up. He wept for hours.

Uncle Ohan said: "Arise, my boy. Chimishkik Sultana will strike at Sassoun. Her troops are already on the march. The heathen will sweep over Sassoun like a torrential flood."

Meherr stood up. He said: "O Lord in heaven, I will kill

her. I will not rest until not a single soul is left alive in Akhlat."

Uncle Toros said: "Akhlat is fortified, and she has an army. It would not be easy to destroy this city."

Uncle Ohan said: "She will try to kill Meherr next."

Meherr said: "Uncle Ohan, you talk as if you were afraid of a woman. Don't we belong to the House of Sassoun? Why, even our tombs frighten the kings of the world. Let's go."

They struck from the bridge. Meherr fell on the troops with drawn sword. His uncles cleaned up the city.

"This is what you get for murdering my father," Meherr said, with every stroke. They chopped them up like so much cabbage. "Sweet work," Uncle Ohan said.

Meherr shouted to his uncles: "Be sure you kill every moving thing in sight. Don't spare even cats or sheep. Kill them all. Chimishkik Sultana can change herself into a cat, a sheep, a fox — into anything. She is a witch."

Meherr scattered and destroyed her army, and caught the queen alive. He tied her to the tail of his horse. Only a few shreds of her hair were left, clinging to his horse's tail, when he rode up to Mount Nemrout to take a look at the burning city, and rode back to his uncles, directing the slaughter.

When they were through, and could not find a single inhabitant alive in the ruins of the city, Meherr saw a cat on top of a minaret, staring down at them. He said: "Look, Chimishkik Sultana changed herself into a cat and is sitting on that minaret." He took aim with his bow and brought the cat down, finally killing the queen. "I have now avenged my father's death," Meherr said. They left Akhlat a rubble of smoky ruins.

Uncle Toros said in his mind: "If we go back to Sassoun with David's body, Khandout might kill herself. She is waiting for us." He said to the others: "Let us tie David's body on the back of his horse, wearing his clothes, and go back pretending he is still alive and we are just playing jereed. We will take his daughter with us and bury them together."

Standing on the tower of the fort, Khandout Khatoun saw

them coming as they raced their horses and hurled their javelins. When they came closer, she saw that David was not moving on his horse. Colicky Vergo raced ahead of the others and was the first to reach the fort. She said:

"The worthless one came back
My bold green David did not."

Vergo hurried up to Khandout and said: "David died in the river without fighting. You are left without your brave David, but you need not be left without a husband." Meaning she could marry him.

Khandout turned to him and said: "O you miserable wretch, you expect me to marry *you,* after David? From this day on the sun will never shine for me again. This world is of no use to me, with David gone."

She leaped from the tower of the fort, and her head struck a rock. They pulled her out of the rock. To this day the people of Sassoun crush parched wheat into bulgur in the big hole made by her head. And where her breasts struck, two jets of water spouted out of the rock, and these two fountains flow to this day. Even now you can see the marks left by her seven braids of hair on the hollow stone that is still there before the fort.

Uncle Toros said, as he dismounted: "Who told Khandout David is dead?"

They said: "Vergo."

"You dog, couldn't you wait and get back to the fort with us?"

Meherr had the bodies of his parents washed and shrouded, and the three caskets bound together. With forty priests, forty vardapets, forty deacons singing hymns, and all the people of Sassoun lamenting their death, he took them to Dzovasar and buried them with a requiem mass side by side in the monastery rebuilt by David. He knelt before his parents' graves and said:

"I bow and invoke thy blessings on him
Who was my father, David of Sassoun
Have mercy O God on his righteous soul.

His words of wisdom I will not forget
The things he taught me by word and by deed
Though I caused him grief and gave them no heed.
I bow and invoke thy blessings on her
Have mercy O God on Khandout Khatoun
Who bore me in her womb, nursed me at her breast
Peace be on her soul, I gave her no rest."

Sassoun was in mourning for seven weeks. May God have mercy
on their souls. May God bless your sweet life and sun.

RAVEN'S ROCK: MEHERR JUNIOR

Have mercy O God, a thousand mercies on Junior Meherr
Have mercy O God, a thousand mercies on Gohar Khatoun
Have mercy O God, a thousand mercies on Uncle Toros
Have mercy O God, a thousand mercies on Uncle Ohan
Have mercy O God, a thousand mercies on Baron Astghik
From cycle to cycle we have now arrived at Meherr's cycle.

Uncle Ohan took David's clothes and armor and gave them
to Meherr. He said: "Son, take these and wear them. You are
a ram of Sassoun. For whom shall I save them?"
Meherr said:

"I wish I were blind and I did not see
My father's helmet with an orphan's eyes
And could wear it myself with a glad heart.
I wish I were blind and I did not see
My father's mailed shirt with an orphan's eyes
And could wear it myself with a glad heart.
I wish I were blind and I did not see
My father's steel boots with an orphan's eyes

And could wear them myself with a glad heart.
I wish I were blind and I did not see
My father's war-horse with an orphan's eyes
And could ride him myself with a glad heart."

When not hunting in the mountains, Meherr was fighting.
He drove the heathen away from the borders of Sassoun. He
slew his own grandfather when he learned the Emir intended
to use him against his own people and make him forget his origin when he lived with him in Tabriz. Meherr continued to
slaughter the heathen.

Meherr went back to the Georgian girl and was King of
Azerbaijan for seven years. He conquered Georgia and Turke-
stan and these countries paid him tribute, and he was well liked
in those parts, and all honored him. Then one day he received
a letter from Uncle Ohan: "Meherr, Kouz-Badin's grandsons have
risen against us and become very bold. I am too old to fight.
Come as soon as you can."

Meherr said to his wife: "Here is my mace. Hang it from
our door. When the pahlevans see it they will think I am home
sleeping and no one will molest you while I am gone."

He rode back to Sassoun, and he was so moved by the sight
of his ancestral city that he wept. It was evening when he arrived and Uncle Ohan had locked his door and gone to bed.

Ohan stirred in his sleep and said: "What is that voice I just
heard?"

His wife Sara said: "What voice? What are you afraid of?
You are in Sassoun and our door is locked."

Ohan said: "Of course I am afraid. I am an old man and my
grandson is not with me."

Meherr called:

> "Dear Uncle Ohan, you took father's place
> I left my kingdom with only my mace
> I handed over to the Georgian maid
> To defend my city against any raid."

His uncle got out of bed and ran to him. He kissed Meherr on the head and said: "Glory be to God. With you here I am not afraid of anything."

Meherr said: "I came secretly. Only God and an angel know. When the sun strikes my mace it flares with light, and nobody would dare come to my door. In the evening candles of bee's wax burn in the house, and their light too would keep marauders away."

Ohan said: "Welcome home, a thousand times welcome. I know you will take your father's place."

"Who is bothering you now?"

"Kouz-Badin's grandsons. Four of them, and all four savage beasts."

"Do you want them dead or alive?"

"Suit yourself, son."

Early the next morning Meherr rode out to Lera-plain. The four grandsons of Kouz-Badin came out against him with volleys of arrows. An arrow struck Jalali in one foot. Meherr cut the arrow with his sword, but part of it was left in the horse's foot. He caught all four Kouz-Badins and brought them to his uncle. They nailed them on the gate of the city, two on each side. Uncle Ohan removed the broken arrow from the foot of the horse, treated the wound, and the foot was as good as new.

The people of Sassoun were happy to see Meherr back, but Colicky Vergo sat firmly on David's throne, and Vergo's sons were jealous of Meherr.

"Uncle Toros, when will Vergo let me succeed my father?"

"Be patient, son. Vergo has been thinking about it. You will replace him as headman sooner or later."

Uncle Toros talked to Vergo about it. "David's son is back with us, and he is even stronger than his father, the whole world dreads Meherr's strength. He is the rightful successor in the Great House of Sassoun."

Vergo put him off. Such requests made him angry.

Meherr's heart was torn by two conflicting thoughts: Should

he punish Vergo, or be patient and wait until Vergo himself let him succeed his father? He was like grain ground between two millstones, convinced Uncle Toros and Uncle Ohan were power-less against Vergo and Vergo would continue to reign in Sassoun.

Meherr asked for permission to return to his city. Ohan's wife had an eye on the boy. Meherr was very good-looking, sweet-blooded, white-skinned, a young man of parts. She said to her husband: "Let Little Meherr stay with us. I will be glad to keep him."

One morning she said to Ohan: "You go hunting and let Little Meherr stay home. I want to do the washing today."

Ohan went to hunt in the mountains and Meherr stayed home. Sara heated a big copperful of water and said: "Little Meherr, pour the water while I take my bath." She thought: "When he sees me naked he will sin in his heart." She took off her clothes and sat in the tub stark naked.

Meherr said: "Mother, how can I pour the water for your bath? I am ashamed. You have nothing on."

"Why be ashamed? Nonsense. I am cold. Hurry."

He closed his eyes and poured the water. Sara wondered as she washed her hair: "Is he looking at me?" She saw that he was covering his eyes with one hand, holding the bowl with the other. She said: "Meherr, why do you close your eyes? Why don't you look at me? Am I so bad to look at? You please me very much. Oh, Meherr, I am tied to an old man who cannot give me a child. Maybe I can have a child by you. I will poison and kill Ohan."

"You are my uncle's wife and like my own mother and sister to me. How can you say such a thing?"

She seized him by the collar and wanted him to comply with her will. He ran out of the house.

Sara tore up her blouse, messed up her hair, scratched her face until it bled, and waited for her husband to come back. He came in with a wild sheep on his shoulder and said: "Wife, where are you?"

She did not meet him at the door and relieve him of his load. She said: "Look. See what your worthless grandson did to me while I was taking my bath. Did you bring me a son or a lover? Kill him. Kill him like a dog."

Uncle Ohan said: "Wife, are you telling the truth? I cannot believe my grandson would do a thing like that. He is the only one left to chastise the heathen. If we send him away, if we lose him, we would be left defenseless, it would be the end of Sassoun, of our race of strongmen."

"If you feel so about him, I will leave you and let him stay, you can have him. Either he goes, or I go."

Uncle Ohan said: "Wife, you know that the law of the Armenian does not allow a man to leave his lawfully wedded wife, and you cannot leave me either. I myself belong to the Great House of Sassoun, I would be disgraced if you leave me. Lock the door. He won't step into this house again."

Meherr came back in the evening and found the door locked. "She did it," he said. He shouted: "Open the door!"

Ohan said: "Go away. Leave town. You do not belong here. There is no place for you in the Great House of Sassoun. A thing like this is unheard of in our nation. May God have mercy on your soul."

Meherr said: "I can kick this door open, wreck this house and send both of you to the bottomless pit, but my father built this house and I don't have the heart to ruin it. Uncle Ohan, your wife is nothing but a whore and a shameless liar."

Meherr went away weeping.

Meherr returned to Azerbaijan. The Georgian girl was dead.

On his way to Aleppo he met forty strongmen riding camels. They looked more like demons. He greeted them. They returned his greeting. They said: "We are forty brothers. Come join us and we will be forty-one brothers."

Meherr said: "I will be glad to be your brother. But tell me, where are you from, where is your city?"

They said: "We are the sons and grandsons of the King of the East."

"Then why don't you live in your city?"

"Our sister will not let us. She sent us away. She rules our city. She is King there."

"Come, brothers, let us go to your city and show your sister to me."

"To tell the truth, she is a man-eater. She has been devouring men from the day she was born. She ate up our parents and all the people in our kingdom."

The forty strongmen went back to their city with him, riding their camels. What he saw was a ruined deserted town. He said: "What kind of kingdom is this, with nobody living here?" He found in a house a copper cauldron with forty handles. He said: "Let each man shoot a wild sheep, and we shall have our supper together." They went to the mountains and each man shot a wild sheep with his bow. They butchered them, skinned them, dumped the carcasses in the cauldron. Meherr kneaded the dough for their bread, using ten sacks of flour, lit the oven, baked the bread. His forty brothers said: "Meherr, you stay here and keep watch until we come back from our exercises in the field."

Meherr sat before the door and presently a tall elderly woman came along and said: "Greetings, cousin." Cousin? He was surprised. "Greetings, aunt," he said. "What do you wish to tell me?"

"May I die for your soul, it is two days now that I have not baked bread in my oven. I was in the mountains picking greens. I am hungry. Give me a piece of bread and I will go."

He said: "Here is the key to the house. Go open the door. You will find the bread baked and the meat cooked. Eat all you want, and go."

She took the key, opened the door and went in. She was in the house for so long that he got up to see what she was doing there. He saw that she had eaten all the bread he baked, and all the meat in the cauldron.

She said: "May I die for your soul, I was so hungry I ate all of it, and I am still hungry."

Meherr thought: "Oh-oh, she must be their man-eating sister." He slapped her, and her head flew off. . . . He sat down at the door and thought: "There is nothing left for my brothers to eat." The forty strongmen came back and saw their sister's severed head. They kissed Meherr's hands and feet and said: "We were helpless against her. We could not recover our city as long as she ruled it.[1] She has devastated our country all the way to Egypt. We brought you here to kill her. Be our new King, and we shall serve you faithfully to the day of our death."

Meherr said: "I want nothing from you. I do not wish to be King. Let one of you be King. I am Meherr, son of David, heirless, and deathless.[2] Let us all go to Baghdad, brothers. I want to see the tomb of my ancestor, Balthasar, who died in Baghdad, after he came back from Copper City."

They all went to Baghdad with him, riding their camels. The city was well built, with many parks and handsome buildings. They met an old man and asked him: "What's new in Baghdad, who is King here?"

The old man said: "The King is a grandson of the Caliphs."

Meherr said: "Show me Balthasar's tomb."

The old man said: "I cannot. It is directly in front of the King's palace."

Meherr rode on to the King's palace. The King stepped out to see the daring warrior who would not dismount before his palace. He asked him: "Who are you?"

"Don't you know who I am? Meherr of Sassoun."

"Oh! Sassoun! Yes, yes, I remember now. It is written in our court records that a man will come from Sassoun and take Baghdad away from us."

Meherr said: "I have no desire to take your city away from

you. I came here because Balthasar belongs to our nation, to the Great House of Sassoun. Will you show me his tomb?"

The King showed him Balthasar's tomb in the royal park. Meherr dismounted and kneeling and bowing prayed before the grave of his ancestor. The marks left by his hands on the marble tombstone are still visible.

The King said: "I wear the crown in this city, but it is not an easy life to be King of Baghdad. I have no rest. It is one war after another. We have so many enemies."

Meherr said: "Who is your worst enemy? Whom do you fear most?"

The King said: "He is a demon, Koup Dev, crippled in one arm, and he has forty pahlevans under him."

Meherr rose up on Friday and went against Koup Dev. It was a day's ride to the demon's stronghold. Koup Dev hurled millstones at him, but Meherr paid no attention. The demon turned and fled into his cave, which was so large ten thousand sheep could not fill it. He said: "Woe to me, I can smell Balthasar's odor, this man is coming to kill me. I know the smell of Sassoun."

Koup Dev lay down and pretended to be sick, moaning from pain.

Meherr entered the cave and said: "What are you moaning for?"

The demon said: "I stayed too long in the sun and got sunstroke. My head aches."

Meherr said: "You are playing sick. There is nothing wrong with you. Get up and fight."

Koup Dev said: "I don't want to fight." He fought only with millstones and did not have a sword.

Meherr said: "Bread and wine, the living God, Marouta's High Mother of God, the Victory Cross on my right arm."

The demon was in tears. "Bread and wine? Ah, you are Balthasar's son!"

"Not his son, but we are related. I am Meherr, son of David."

When the demon heard David's name, he stood up and fought. They fought savagely for three hours, and Meherr struck off his head. He was going to kill also the demon's forty warriors, who crowded fearfully in a corner of the cave, when they took off their clothes and he found himself standing before forty naked girls. Each gave him her patronymic, and all forty were daughters of kings. He took these forty girls Koup Dev held captive, and the demon's head, and delivered them to the King in Baghdad. He said: "Now you can reign in peace."

The King said: "Since you killed my worst enemy, it is only proper that from now on you be King of Baghdad."

He said: "No, thank you. I am Meherr, son of David, and I have to be moving along. I am heirless and deathless."

"Then tell me what you want and you shall have it. I will do anything for you, Meherr."

He said: "I have forty brothers with me, sons and grandsons of the King of the East, and I brought you these forty beautiful girls who were Koup Dev's captives. Call forty priests to marry them to my forty brothers, and build a Christian church for me in Baghdad. I want nothing else from you."

By the King's order a great church with forty altars was built on Balthasar's tomb and dedicated to Saint Sargis. To this day this church is called Saint Sargis. The forty girls married Meherr's forty brothers, and the King said:

"Meherr, now it is your turn to marry and settle down. I will give you my own daughter as wife."

He said: "Thank you, King, but I cannot marry your daughter, I am heirless and deathless."

Meherr left Baghdad with his forty brothers and their brides. One of the forty strongmen became King of the East. Meherr bid them farewell and went on to Jezira, where a hundred and forty rivers mingle to form the great river of Jezira. This river had flooded and destroyed the city three times. Meherr flung huge boulders into the river and divided its channel. He built dams and dikes and thus saved the city from future floods. He built an impregnable fortress with white towers which will last to the end of the world.

Meherr mounted his horse and rode out to the country of King Pajik. He dismounted, pitched his tent. The King was informed of his arrival; he was told Meherr of Sassoun would attack and destroy his city. Taking his vizier, his deputy and counselors with him the King came to Meherr and said: "I made a pact with your father when he fought Misra Melik."

Meherr said: "What pact?"

"We vowed to unite our two families through marriage. His son was to marry my daughter. God blessed David with a son like you, and I have a beautiful daughter. The King of Aleppo has wanted to marry her for the past seven years. The King of the West and other kings have asked for her hand. Will you marry her?"

"I will, if I like her. But if I don't, I will strike."

Meherr went with the King to see his daughter. He liked her, and she liked him. Her name was Gohar[3] Khatoun. He stayed in his tent. Early the next morning a warrior in a scarlet costume, riding a golden-brown steed, pulled up before his tent. "Meherr, you will get sunstroke," he said.

"What can I do if my tent is too small?"

"It is not small, it is big enough, but man, you belong to a race of giants!"

"Oh, well, let me have my sleep."

"Meherr, get up. I am the King's son. I want to test your strength and courage. I am not willing to have my sister Gohar be given to you as ransom. The camel also is big and strong, but they have to bring him down to his knees before they load him. I want to see what's so good about you."

"Very well, what do you have in mind? Tell me," said Meherr.

"I will hang a dark hair with a bead at the end from a tree in the arena. If you can cut the hair with an arrow then you have the skill to match your size and strength, and I will not

oppose your marriage, Gohar is yours. If you fail, I will strike off
your head."

Meherr took his bow and arrows, mounted his horse and went
to the arena with him. He planted a knee on the ground, called
upon his Lord, and shot an arrow from his bow: it cut the hair,
and the bead fell to the ground.

Meherr returned to his tent. A servant of the King brought
him a whole roast sheep placed on a big mound of white pilav
and a large jug of wine for breakfast. After he finished eating
Meherr went back to sleep.

The next morning another warrior, dressed in black, rode up
to his tent and said: "Meherr, you coward, I could pin you down
on your back if I did not feel so sorry for you."

"If you are so brave why didn't you come against me with
your King when I was ready to strike the other day? You could
have shown your courage then."

"I am the King's second son. I am against your marrying my
sister Gohar unless you can prove to me you are worthy of her."

"How can I prove it?"

"I shall lie on my back and place my ring on my forehead,
setting it on the stone. If you can shoot it off my forehead you
can marry my sister. If you cannot, you lose your head."

"I am ready," said Meherr.

The King's second son took off his ring, lay on his back at
some distance from Meherr, placed the ring on his forehead.
Once again Meherr called upon his Lord, took aim with his
bow, and the ring flew away.

"Meherr, you did it. I will keep my word. Come, let us go
to the palace."

Meherr was received with many honors at the King's palace.

He realized later that they were not her brothers, but Gohar
herself testing him. He married her, and the wedding was celebrated for seven days and nights. They ate, drank, and made
merry. At night, as they went to bed in her castle, Gohar Khatoun put a sharp naked sword between them.

She said: "The King of the West to whom I was promised collects tribute from us. If you can bring me his head, we can live as man and wife."

The next morning Meherr rode out against the King of the West. The King saw him coming, like a mountain on a mountain, and was terrified. Meherr and his horse slaughtered the King's troops and by nightfall the battle was over. Meherr whirled around and rode back to Gohar with the King's head. He said: "Your father does not have to pay tribute any more."

King Shapi-Arkah came out against them. Gohar said: "He is bent on revenge. He will kill my father, kill you, and drag me away by force if he can." Meherr worked out a ruse. He disguised himself as the son of an Armenian parish priest and went to Shapi-Arkah. He said: "May the King live long, I have been sent by Gohar Khatoun to inform you that she will marry you if all the males in your city old enough to use a spoon come join the bridal party for your wedding."

"Good," the King said. "Tomorrow morning go through my city as my herald and call all males old enough to use a spoon to join the bridal party for my wedding."

The next morning Meherr collected all the males of fighting age and led them out of the city walls. Then he turned on them and hacked them down with his sword. Gohar Khatoun, riding out of her castle in battle gear, struck from the other side and joined the slaughter. She said: "If you pass under Meherr's sword, I will not kill you. Expect no mercy if you do not."

All of them passed under Meherr's sword, all, except the King. She slashed off his head. They returned to their castle in a merry mood, and went to bed. When they were not fighting they made love.

The King of Aleppo came to Sassoun and said to Uncle Ohan: "There is a man in my country who kidnapped the girl I had chosen to be my bride and will not return her to me. Give me one of your famed pahlevans to help me recover my bride, and I will give you seven cities as reward."

Ohan picked Vergo's son, Baron Astghik for this task. He gave him a winged horse like the Colt Jalali, and a sword from the arsenal of Sassoun that struck lightning. Baron Astghik girt on his sword, mounted his fiery horse, and flying between heaven and earth swooped down over Aleppo as the morning sun bloomed and flowered in the sky.

Meherr smelled the presence of a kinsman near the castle and stayed in, would not go out to fight. Gohar Khatoun said: "Why are you so gloomy and silent? You were always so gay and happy, and came back laughing and talking from every battle we fought. And now you sit here doing nothing and won't say a word."

Meherr said: "I am not fighting today."

Gohar Khatoun said: "Then I would have to fight the King of Aleppo alone."

"You can do as you like. I am not fighting. I will stay in this morning."

"Please go out and fight."

"I will not, I said."

"Meherr, aren't you ashamed of yourself? How can you let me fight the King of Aleppo alone?"

"Very well, I will fight him, but promise me you will keep all the doors and windows shut during the battle until I come back."

She shut the doors and windows, and spun wool by candlelight.

Meherr got up, slung on his arms, took his bow and dashed out of the castle holding his shield over his head. Vergo's son met him in the arena for single combat. All Meherr could do against this warrior was to stay under his shield. The missiles of his adversary battered on his shield like hailstones, bounced off and struck the ground with such force that they reached the bottomless pits under the earth. This man always struck from above, forcing Meherr to strike from below, but Meherr could not reach him with his sword and found himself powerless in this kind of warfare. His enemy flew back and forth on his winged horse with sweeping strokes of his sword that hissed and crackled with fiery sparks. What saved Meherr was the Holy Emblem in his breast pocket.

Thunderflashes shook the castle and Gohar heard the dreadful sound of the fighting that went on outside. She said: "Why all this thunder and lightning? The sky is clear." She was puzzled, and curious. She opened a window and looked out. She saw a blazing whirlwind of horses and swords and maces crashing, of missiles shattered to fiery fragments over Meherr's shield as he cowered under it, and the rain of fire that poured over his head reaching down to the bottomless pits under the earth. She said: "So this was the reason why Meherr did not want to fight this morning."

Gohar Khatoun was a learned woman, a reader. She opened a book and found out who this warrior was. To put an end to this terrible combat she bared her white bosom and leaning out the window called aloud to Baron Astghik:

"Welcome, Uncle, a thousand times welcome, welcome!
Stop pouring fire over his head, kill me instead
Don't torture him, he is so young, and wreck my home
My life is yours, I will, Uncle, gladly keep you
In my bosom, if you only spare my Meherr."

Meherr heard her and said: "I told her to keep the windows shut. You can't trust a woman's word." He was furious with his wife for saying "My life is yours, I will keep you in my bosom."

Baron Astghik saw her white breasts and heard her plea. He stopped fighting. Meherr did not. And, as though to spite his wife, drew his bow and shot at him from below the belly of the winged horse. The poison-smeared arrow smashed through the horse, sending him high into the air and came out of the top of the warrior's head, and Astghik crashed to the ground with his horse.

"May God wreck your home, you are Meherr. I was struck by a kinsman. Only a kinsman could bring me down."

It was only now that Baron Astghik recognized Meherr.

He said: "Meherr, it is a rule in Sassoun, an old tradition with us, that when one of us dies he should have his head resting on the knee of a kinsman before he gives up his soul to God."

Meherr put Baron Astghik's head on his knee, listened to the death-rattle in his throat. As his kinsman gave up his soul to God, Meherr fell down in a swoon.

When he came to he could not forget what his wife said to Baron Astghik. He buried this man and said to Gohar Khatoun: "I vow that for seven years you will be nothing but a mother and sister to me. I was cursed by my father, and now I have killed a kinsman. I will not come back until I wipe the heathen off the face of the earth, and clear my conscience. Hang my mace from the door of the castle and nobody will dare harm you while I am gone."

He mounted his horse, and rode off, thirsting for more pagan blood.

He slaughtered the heathen for seven years and destroyed their temples.

When Meherr came back to the castle seven years later he found his mace hanging from the door exactly as he left it. He opened the door and went in. He called out to his wife: "Gohar, I am back. Where are you, can't you hear me?" He found her seated on their throne, dead, holding a paper in her hand. He took it and read: "Meherr, when you come back and find me dead please bury me in Sassoun, next to Khandout Khatoun. Do not leave me in this heathen country."

Meherr took Gohar's body to Sassoun and buried her in the monastery next to his mother's grave on Mount Marouta. He had forty requiem masses sung over his wife and parents, and for all the dead in Sassoun.

Uncle Ohan was no longer living, he was among the dead.

Meherr got up and went to his father's grave. He was going to kneel before it and pray when he changed his mind, mounted his horse, and rode off, not knowing where to go, what to do. He had not gone far when he saw that the feet of his horse sank in the earth. He said: "Hoy-hoy! The earth can no longer support me, as my father predicted. This is the end. The vein was pulled from my loins and I have remained heirless upon this earth, unable to propagate the seed of Sassoun. And I am deathless. I have to wait for Christ's return on judgment day to save my soul."

He turned back, came and knelt before David's grave, crying out in anguish:

"Blessed is our Lord God, great is his mercy.
Rise up father dear from your dreamless sleep
I am frozen numb on this wintry peak
Tell me where to go, O where can I dwell
On this ancient earth crumbling beneath me
When I am alone and I have no share
No part in Sassoun, and without an heir
Expelled from our House by my own kin
I wander around with no place to rest
Longing for your words, your fatherly smell
Living in exile, homeless everywhere."

A voice answered him from David's grave:

"Son, what can I do, son, what can I do?
I have lost my strength, my hair and my sight
Serpents and scorpions have made me their nest
I am powerless now to help you find rest.
Stop roaming around, your journey's at end
You are immortal, deathless on this earth
There is no freedom from all your torment
Save in Raven's Rock. Go to Raven's Rock
That's the door to knock. Wait till judgment day
The end of this world. It will be destroyed

And a new world built to support the feet
Of your fiery horse. When that happens, son
And you ride again, the whole world is yours."

Meherr turned to his mother's grave:

"Rise up mother dear, rise up from your sleep
The child of your bosom, your own son Meherr
Is back at your tomb, cast off from Sassoun.
I went everywhere and I never found
A mother like you, to you I am bound
With my heart and soul, I never did meet
A mother so good, so patient and sweet.
Tell me what to do, I have lost my way."

A voice answered him from the tomb of the lady Khandout:

"Son, what can I do, son, what can I do?
I have lost my looks, my hair and my sight
Serpents and scorpions have made me their nest
I am powerless now to help you find rest.
We live in this world and then pass away
That's the end for all, but you are without
This one last comfort of mortality
And you do not have an heir of your own.
Stop wandering around and go there, go there
Where your bread is baked and your meal is cooked
And you never need fear of going hungry
In the Rock of Van, Raven's Rock, Meherr."

The voice stopped speaking. Meherr rose sobbing to his feet,
mounted his horse, and rode off to find the Rock, praying on
his way:

"O merciful God
Take pity on me
Let me get to Van
And to Raven's Rock."

He did not know where it was. He was starved, had nothing to eat. He rode in the mountains of Akhlat and went up to the summit of Mount Sipan, looking for Raven's Rock. He wandered around Lake Van. In the great gorge of Vostan a prince caught him and his horse and tied them up. Meherr remembered his prayer: "Bread and wine, the living God, Marouta's High Mother of God, the Victory Cross on my right arm." He drew his sword and cut the chains, the iron and gold, and freed himself and his horse from the clutches of this prince.

The earth shook and gave way under the feet of his horse. The Colt Jalali sank deeper in the crumbling sod. It came up to his knees. Meherr urged him on, and on, and reached the plain of Van. "Keep me or fight me," he said to God in his despair. God sent seven mounted angels to fight him. The Lightning Sword had no effect on the angels. They tortured him. He fought, in vain, from noon to sundown. Then as he looked up he saw a talking raven of fiery color flying over the plain. He took aim with his bow and shot an arrow that struck the raven, and the wounded bird flew off and disappeared in a cave, pursued by Meherr. He halted before the Rock, on Tospa's hill. Swinging his mace he said with tears in his eyes: "If I can split this rock open, I am not guilty. If I cannot, I am guilty."

He struck, and split the Rock wide open. God took him in. He rode into the cave and dismounted on firm ground. As the two halves of the Rock came together and it closed over him Meherr heard a voice say: "You shall stay in this Rock until a grain of wheat is as big as the berry of sweet-briar, and a grain of barley grows to the size of a hazel-nut. When that day comes, you will be allowed to go out."

Meherr found shelter at last, and was freed of his misery. Uncle Toros died of grief when he heard Meherr was shut up in Raven's Rock.

Sassoun's stock continues to this day and many brave men still come out of Sassoun, descendants of these Daredevils.

EPILOGUE

It is called Raven's Rock because the raven entered it. They say the Rock opens twice a year, on the Festival of Roses and on Ascension Day.[4] When the Rock opens Meherr springs out on his horse and rides in an hour a distance of forty days to see if the world has changed and the earth will hold him, but the feet of his horse start sinking again, and Meherr returns to the cave. He is out only for two hours.

They say he has built a church and monastery in the Rock, and he and his horse live on the manna that falls from heaven. Once, on Easter Sunday, a man said to his daughter: "Go to church, light this candle and come back with God's blessed light." The girl went out and saw lights burning in the Rock. She thought it was a church. She went in. The door was open. Just as she lighted her candle the two halves of the Rock came together. She ate manna with Meherr, and was not hungry for a year. On the following Easter the Rock opened again and she came home with her lighted candle. Her father asked her: "Where have you been all this time? A whole year has passed since I sent you to church." She said: "Father, I just went to church and came back." This made him wonder. He asked: "Did you see anybody there?" "I saw only a man and his horse." "Did you see anything before the entrance?" "A walnut tree. Nothing else." "What did you eat there?" "Something like small round wafers that fell from the sky. I saw this man eating it, and I ate it myself." She had not been hungry since then. They realized it was Meherr with his horse.

They say when the Rock opened on another day, a shepherd went in and saw a huge warrior sitting there, watching the wheel of fortune. The shepherd asked him: "Meherr, when are you coming out of here?" Meherr turned to him and said: "The earth will not keep me if I go out. As long as the world stays evil the earth itself is deceitful. I cannot live in such a world. When this world is destroyed, and rebuilt, when a grain of wheat is as big as the berry of sweet-briar and a grain of barley grows to the size of a hazel-nut, I will be out of here, but not before." The shepherd got out before the two halves of the Rock came together and it closed again.

They say the black water that drips from the Rock is the urine of the Colt Jalali, and people have heard his mighty whinney echoing through the cave.

God have mercy on the Great House of Sassoun
May Marouta's High Mother of God
Remain forever firm and bright on her rocky foundation.

NOTES

[1] This man-eating matriarch may represent in an allegorical manner an early primitive stage of social organization in Armenia when, perhaps, women ruled. We do not have here a realistic scene. There is a large component of legend in the fourth and final cycle.

[2] Meherr's inability to have children of his own makes it impossible for him to be king — this is the implication of his repeated refusals to be king. As a king he must have an heir.

[3] Gohar: Jewel.

[4] The Rock miraculously opens on Ascension Day and the Festival of Roses (*Vardavar*), when miracles happen. Armenians celebrate these holidays out of doors. On Ascension Day girls fill their pitchers with water drawn from a milk-fountain (as in our monastery in Trebizond) and each girl throws a ring, or earring, a bracelet, a brooch or some other personal article into the pitcher, meanwhile making a wish. The mouth of the pitcher is closed with roses, violets, and other flowers — seven different flowers often being another requirement — and the pitcher is hidden during the night to expose it to the influence of the stars. Boys and young men prowl around looking for it, and if they find it, they will not give it back to the girls without getting a few kisses in return. The next morning the girls sit in a circle on the grass, the youngest holding the pitcher in her lap and sitting in the center. They sing songs, making fun of young men. One of the girls makes a prediction by quoting a popular saying or proverb, and another girl draws out an article from the pitcher. The prediction just pronounced is supposed to come true in the life of the girl who owns the article, and as generally it has to do with romance or marriage, shrieks, applause, laughter, accompany the drawing.

During the Festival of Roses men and women, the young and old, gather around milk-fountains and other springs, or everybody is out in the streets, and people sprinkle water on one another — rose water in the old days — and fly doves. In ancient Armenia the dove was a sacred bird dedicated to the goddess of Love and Beauty.

Invoke God's mercy on Dzovinar
Forty prayers for Sanasar
Invoke God's mercy on Balthasar
Forty prayers for Golden-Braids
Invoke God's mercy on Uncle Toros
Forty prayers for Uncle Ohan
Invoke God's mercy on Great Meherr
Forty prayers for Armaghan
Invoke God's mercy on brave David
A thousand prayers for David
Invoke God's mercy on Khandout Khatoun
Forty prayers for Little Meherr
Invoke God's mercy on Gohar Khatoun
Forty prayers for our master
Who told this tale, blessings to all
The great and small who heed his words
O Merciful God.